THE NEW

DAD HACKS SERIES:

3 in 1

What to expect from pregnancy to Infant. A parent's guide for men with tips and hacks that every first time dad needs

By William Harding

Table of Contents

Part I

Book 1: NEW DAD HACKS

Part II

Book 2: NEW DAD BABY HACKS

Part III

Book 3: NEW DAD JOURNAL

Just For you!

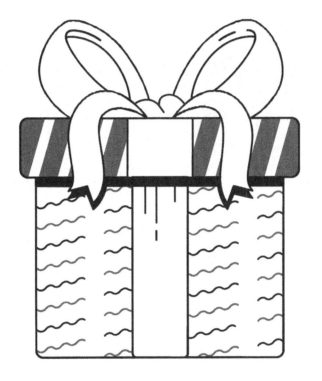

A FREE GIFT TO OUR READERS

10 Step **Action** plan that you can download now. Feel confident and prepared for your new born right now!

http://williamhardingauthor.com/

A MODERN **4 STEP PREGNANCY GUIDE** FOR FIRST TIME DADS,
USE THESE SHORTCUTS TO HELP YOU FEEL PREPARED
AND TRANSITION INTO FATHERHOOD

NEW DAD
HACKS

WILLIAM HARDING

NEW DAD HACKS

A Modern 4 Step Pregnancy Guide for First Time Dads, Use These Shortcuts to Help You Feel Prepared and Transition Into Fatherhood

By William Harding

Introduction

The thing that shocked me most about becoming a dad the first time was the feeling of helplessness. No one sent me the memo. Somehow, I figured that when I heard that baby cry in the delivery room, the challenge of the previous nine months was over. I expected it would be the time I could sigh in relief. All the stuff I hadn't been expecting over the last six months of life-changing events — mostly explored through my partner's emotions, cravings — would revert like clearing the cache on my browser. The rest would take care of itself. Or at least my wife would take care of it until the kid could talk and play catch.

Part of the reason I had no idea what to expect was the fact that birthing classes mostly covered everything up to the moment of birth. They covered a lot of practical things but ended up being all about what we would experience during the pregnancy from mom's point of view, packing a hospital bag, and preparing for the main event that was like a vacation at your in-laws. There were no dad-only nights where you got the lowdown on hormonal changes and the importance of shopping for a whole new wardrobe for months on end. The fact that the shape of my partner became alien was the easiest part to deal with because a lot of other things changed. Finances had already started to change, and many things shifted gradually and dramatically toward a baby orientation that I tried to limp through while supporting my spouse, who seemed to innately know how everything was supposed to work. Her confidence and knowledge didn't exactly rub off.

I learned to strap disposable diapers on a dummy; it wasn't very hard; nothing was moving. I even studied up on the finer points of fitting cloth diapers. It was an art similar to that of folding a flag. I passed the test in class, got my boy scout badge, and graduated. When I jabbed the dummy with the giant safety pin, it didn't scream or bleed or make me feel guilty. The dummy wasn't crying and peeing and writhing and pooing again just when I got the diaper off or just when I got it back on. The actual event of changing a diaper on something live was like trying to put a wetsuit on an otter that would rather be swimming. In reality, it was sometimes hard to figure out what I was supposed to clean first because the octopus of unpredictability had been released. Not only did I not know what to clean, but I didn't know what I was supposed to clean it with.

The first few times when my wife handed me the baby, I held it out at arm's length with two hands and stared at it like I was looking for a place to set down. It was like a gifted garden gnome that some friends gave me, and they were coming over for a backyard barbecue, and I didn't want them to feel bad that I ignored their generosity. As I held it out, it invariably started crying and had to be rescued from my grip, which was too hot, too cold, or too much like broken glass. Later I came to find that when you learned to warm up to the baby, it learned to warm up to you. Simple things don't always come to mind first when internally you are panicking about what you are doing wrong. Worse, you are the mythical man who won't stop to ask directions — sometimes even rejecting perfect instructions from a GPS. Often what you don't know, your spouse might, and surely someone else on the planet already does. It's a baby, something the earth's population says was done at least billions of times before.

I didn't have the tools, breasts, or whatever makes mothers, mothers, and dads like animated cacti. My wife would hand it to me, and it was like flipping a switch to tell it to cry. It was like the experience was some life lesson it had to go through to learn about life's cruelties, and I was its personal dungeon of pain. The baby had to learn that, during life, comfort was going to go to some other part of the house now and again, and you have to accept you needed to wait for solace to return.

Most of the real problem ended up being the lack of information. No one walked up to me after I handed out the cigars, pulled me aside, and said, "Hey, William, I've got some news for you." That sage advice I might expect from a buddy about what I got myself into wasn't on its way in person, in a text, or email. It was easy to see that friends I used to hang out with after work on Fridays started to become extinct when they got the news they were about to have a kid. They just dropped off the map not long after that, and I didn't see them anymore. I didn't realize they found out they had a family and their responsibilities changed, and I certainly hadn't had my opportunity to know what that entailed. They were a deafening silence dealing with their own adjustments hung up on the exact communal phrase: "this isn't going the way I expected." Their new cloak of stressors was something they signed up for and might even have been excited about. Like me, the only way they could take on the weight without collapsing was to double-up on the support of their partner and try to become a student of the changes that were going on.

Realistically, I knew there were sacrifices I was going to have to make in return for the gift of bringing a child into our lives. I just didn't know which sacrifices they were or how to handle them. If you take a look around, it is evident that people live through the experience of having children all the time, and some of them are men. I had no idea about the more subtle ways to test my ability to maintain my emotional maturity and composure. I was forced to absorb some duties that I certainly never mastered before I was married and that my spouse assumed the bulk of during the early part of our relationship. Looking from a distance, nothing suggested it was time to start a marathon study for an exam on becoming an adult.

Luckily we were expecting to be expecting. We were trying. Even that was a little strange as romance took on a whole different dimension when it was guided by a thermometer that told my partner when she was "ready." I've tried to do that, and it doesn't work very well. It was as if a third wheel entered into the relationship and some of what was fun (it still was) became an obligation driven by an inanimate object. That was just the beginning of the changes we needed to experience as a couple accepting our entrance into this new phase of our relationship.

For those men who happen to encounter this experience by surprise, that is a whole other level of revelation. Some people call it shock and awe. That's usually used in war and a precursor to PTSD. You'll be shocked at the news, wondering if you heard the right thing, and then everything will go a bit numb and dark around the edges as you discover tunnel vision. If your significant other just handed you a copy of this book and she didn't tell you the results of the second pregnancy test she took, you can only guess why she left it in your hands. Surprise!

Whether the news of fatherhood was planned or a total surprise, your experiences, as the situation slowly evolves, doesn't have to be shock and awe; you CAN manage the changes. My second child was way easier than the first, which is pretty much the rule for everything. The difference was I'd already been through the gauntlet. I found out I still had a few things to learn, but it was far less daunting because of the experience I already had. I would have been better at it if I had started with the second one. Regretfully, this isn't a box of chocolates. You've got to handle the arrival of your children in order—no magic pills or do-overs. Beyond the news of your successful conception and cigars and birthing classes, you need a short course for dads like you. This book is your guide to joining the Dad's Club. The journey starts by just putting one foot in front of the other.

The long, eventful, and rewarding journey you are about to enter is the life of being a father. It all becomes a lot easier when you know the things you need to know because the unexpected surprises won't be there. You can engage in and enjoy the process of learning about the new little adornment to life's experience. This could be your path to experience a whole new type of joy, and, when approached with some savvy, you can experience greater intimacy in your partnership as you strengthen bonds and responsibilities that ultimately tie you together. This book is your map, a guide to help inform you about what may be in store for your future as a new dad; you will be far better equipped for this journey with a few hours of committed reading.

"Every dad, if he takes time out of his busy life to reflect upon his fatherhood, can learn ways to become an even better dad." — Jack Baker

My name is William, and I will be your tour guide. I am the veteran of participating in the experience of bringing no fewer than three new lives into this world. While I was innocent, stressed, and occasionally overwhelmed during the first expedition, I eventually made the adjustments and absorbed my new roles as a father and spouse. Not only that, I wasn't swallowed by the experience of becoming a father as I first felt was going to be the case. I was lucky enough to have a good job that gave me some freedoms that helped cushion the changes I was bound to go through, but even without that, I know now that everything would still have been OK. It would have been even better if I'd had worked harder to gain more insight. But that I was able to manage it walking through the experience and being blindsided at every turn means that you have an advantage that I didn't.

Part of the reason for digging in to write this book is my experience. I know it doesn't have to be a long, strange trip to work through the evolution of your immediate family. Looking back at my experience gave me confidence in approaching the next two wonderful gifts in the expansion of our clan from a nucleus of just two into the group of five I now adore and enjoy. When I found my good friend happily handing out cigars, I stepped up. After he'd made that initial announcement of expecting an addition to his family, I did what I'd hoped someone would have done for me. I put my arm over his shoulder and said, "Hey, Alex, I got some news for you." I offered some encouragement, but more than that, I offered to be there to coach him, answer his questions and talk about the stuff he was going to go through. I often beat him to the punch and sent him a message or three about where his life was heading when I recognized frustration or another milestone.

Seeing his response and feeling like I'd helped him, I was quicker to offer my support to my next buddy, who was setting out his wagon train to the wild west. Eventually, I was inspired to start an informal group for men, specifically for guys who no longer met up on Fridays after work because they were expecting their first. The goal was to help men seek some comradery, share experiences, and learn about what to expect as they traveled into unknown territory. More, it helped bring back some friends that had fallen into pregnancy and parenthood but neglected their own emotional well-being.

It has been seven years since my journey into this phase of my life began. The joy of that experience and the pleasure I took in helping others weather the storm of surprises brought me here to a point where I hope to help even more newcomers to the world of fatherhood. I know I've gotten better at being a husband and a father, and I am sure that I can help others learn from my struggles and successes in the challenges ahead. Like achieving success in your career, studies, or on the playing field, it will take some effort, but the results will be worth it. Confidence will give you more space to enjoy the experience and let that attitude of joy bleed into everything else you do while making you an enthusiastic participant instead of a casualty.

Let's get started on this new adventure. It may be a little like sky diving the first time, but we're jumping out of the plane in tandem, and I've checked the equipment and got you covered. It is a thrill I guarantee you will live through, and perhaps you'll reach out and pay it forward.

Parenting and Partnering Power

"Parenting and Partnering Power" are short focus sections at the end of every chapter. They are here to help guide you by emphasizing essential points and tell you what you should be doing to help yourself become a super-dad. Read every one of these and set yourself into action to get the most from the book.

The first task to activate your parenting power is to dedicate some time every day to get this book read from cover to cover. If you can only set aside 20 minutes a day, you will get it done in about a week (about 200 words per minute). Don't just breeze through to get it done. Concentrate on what you are reading and let it sink in. If you are pretty sure you glazed over something, don't cheat yourself; make a point to reread the sections the next day instead of moving on just to get through it. Dedication to reading is a little investment in the rest of your life, and it will be worth it.

Chapter One:

Yikes! You're Going To Be a Father

You just heard that you are going to be a father. No matter where the news came from, whether you've been looking forward to hearing those words or becoming a dad is a total surprise; you will likely be experiencing a wave of emotions, like a guy walking into the surf at the seaside. Whether you step into the violent uncertainty of ocean breakers or gentle lapping wavelets in a lagoon depends on the beach. Still, either way, there are rip tides and scary things under the water that were just waiting for you to get your feet wet.

One good piece of advice to follow, no matter how the surf is behaving, don't go swimming alone!

When you find out your partner is pregnant, you will have mixed emotions that can run to extremes. After all, it will be the day you realize something has definitively changed, and it will significantly affect your life from this point forward. This point in your life is a little like stepping off the landing at a bungee jump. The initial reaction might be fear, joy, surprise, trepidation — I'm not going to try and limit what you feel. Unless you've got narcolepsy, one thing you won't do is sleep through that initial moment of "what do I do now?"

The importance of empathy can not be stressed enough. The pregnancy is not something she is solely responsible for. It is something that you are both about to go through. Being empathetic and caring starts from the moment, you learn about the pregnancy. That moment when you hear the news, you might be tempted to be a bonehead and blurt out something that immediately comes to mind.

* "Are you serious?"
* "How did that happen?"
* "I thought you were on birth control."
* "Is it mine?"

This is not recommended as a starting point. If you've already started with the bonehead move, time to step back, regroup and grovel. You had a moment of pessimism that passed, and now you can beg forgiveness to clear the air and restore the regularly scheduled tempest. Depending on the situation, she may not have expected you to be overjoyed, but she will expect you to be part of her team. That may not take much more than a smile and saying, "I love you."

Your Partner, Your Strength

Something that often seems to calm a restless soul is finding someone who shares your perspective. The wonderful thing about pregnancy is that you and your partner are immersed in the reality of the pregnancy and tethered to it simultaneously. You are both in the same boat (yes, another analogy relating to water). If she doesn't make the first move to start talking about how she feels or asking you how you are with the news, there is nothing that's stopping you from sharing how you feel or trying to draw her out. Someone has to take up the oar, start the motor, or lift the sail. The ship has to get underway. Someone has to steer the boat. The crew has to work together. Some of the responsibility will be assumed automatically, but communication is imperative as you sail away into open waters. A lot can go wrong if the team is not in harmony with each other and the motion of the sea.

You may be used to taking the lead in many parts of your partnership, but on this excursion, you don't have to be the captain. A woman will probably be more prepared for what's on the horizon. Your partner will have paid more attention to her friends who are having children. She will likely have gained a sense of nurturing and nesting as a part of her nature and experience. You, on the other hand, are like a man sent out to buy tampons. You may be looking at pregnancy like a bunch of shelves loaded with boxes of brands, things you have no experience with. If you are like me, rather than asking your partner for direction, you'll wait to watch a few women make their selections while pretending to be looking at something elsewhere in the aisle. Then you can use the knowledge gained as a voyeur to come to a conclusion.

You may be sad to hear that the aforementioned male response to never ask for directions is the wrong response to your partner's superior knowledge of a subject. This new phase of your relationship is an opportunity to learn more about one another. One thing she will appreciate is that you show interest in what is happening. She may even understand that you seem to respect her knowledge of what it is like to be a woman and how she feels about the experience of pregnancy and childbirth. You may have goofed up and brought home the wrong box of tampons, but pregnancy is a much bigger thing that you aren't just going back to the store to exchange. It is OK not to know what being a pregnant woman is like, especially if you are a man. Asking your most intimate friend about it is sharing and bonding that can lead to sometimes alien things like respect and understanding.

At the same time, when you flounder in your ignorance and timidly approach her to share her wisdom, don't think she'll be all cool, calm, and collected. There are reasons for that, including raging hormones and her insecurities and uncertainty. This is something that she will physically experience for the first time, and that experience is far more immediate. You will both be stressed — be that from different perspectives. Any time of stress is a time where people are more apt to expose themselves emotionally, and sometimes being calm and rational is not the first step. Some might consider emotional exposure to ultimately be what a relationship is all about. One of the best things you can do is work at trying to explore the phenomenon together.

Before you start out with the map held upside-down, stress is not a bad thing. It is simply arousal that makes you more aware and alert to your surroundings. It is something you can use to your advantage to be more mindful and live in the moment. You are more likely to accept and achieve in a stressful situation if you take ownership of it rather than letting it run over you. In this case, taking ownership is sharing the experience with your partner. Working together through planning stages, sharing fears, joys, ideas, and responsibilities can help make your bond stronger. That will help throughout the pregnancy and into the years of learning the ropes of dealing with the baby, toddler, child, and teen as the wonder you created emerges and matures. It is a time to build strength and stability with headlights looking into the future.

The Physical Burden

In most ways, the physical burden of the pregnancy will be on the woman. She is carrying the living wonder in a symbiotic relationship as it grows inside her, and she is experiencing unfamiliar changes to her hormonal balance and physique. These changes can easily affect mood, endurance, and behaviors in ways that no one can predict. She may be alarmed and anxious about some of the changes, and it may be challenging for her to control her emotions. It is important to realize that while you may not be the one changing, you will experience the effects of the change either indirectly in her response to you because of how she feels or how the changes in your lifestyle affect you.

You may need to take up the slack when she is not feeling well and pitch in. Almost certainly, this is going to place additional demands on your resources such as time, energy, and sleep. This may mean skipping a card game, watching a sporting event, or a favorite TV show. It could mean waking a bit earlier to drop in a load of laundry or taking a shopping list out to the store after work. The effort will be easier to take on if you approach your partner with empathy and the situation with the understanding of the reward.

If you play your part true to the noble father-to-be, there is a good chance you may get pretty exhausted and even confounded by new responsibilities. These extra duties should never become a point of contention or resemble a contest of one-upmanship. You are trading the burden she has accepted by accepting some of your own to try to balance out the scale. While I was lucky enough to have some culinary background and could be called on in a pinch to cook, my household chores before my partner's pregnancy were generally delegated as "things that needed to be fixed." After pregnancy and my being steadfast in the idea that I didn't need any stinking directions, I didn't bother my partner with questions about doing laundry. That fear of admission led to parts of our white wardrobe shading pink. As it turns out, I needed lessons in folding clothes her way, which was more artful than my bachelor technique of piling things in a drawer. Back in the day, as long as the drawer would shut, the mission was accomplished.

Suppose you can bring yourself to always have the addition to your family as the light at the end of the tunnel, a muzzle on when a joke might be too campy, a mask of stoicism or empathy for those moments where the evil wants to erupt. In that case, you will dilute tension, quell turbulence, and avoid all earthquakes. Believe me, she is far more challenged than you are and at least equally stressed. Take the time to ask how she is doing and listen to what she is saying without flipping the channels on the TV. Your life is no longer only about you, and it isn't only about you and your partner. It is about engaging with the person you chose to live your life with to get through this experience with as much enjoyment as possible, as it leads to the next incredible stage of life together with a child.

The more you do pamper your partner, the more comfortable *you* will be and the more she will appreciate your effort. Bring her flowers, write a love note, and let her know you are excited about the future. You can't take her physical burden away from her, but you can help with the emotional burden by going just above and beyond at that moment where you think you did enough. Imagine if she just decided one day that carrying a baby was too much trouble. She's in no place to affect half measures, and neither are you.

You will have a lot of learning to do, and different stages of the pregnancy will require different levels of sainthood. If your mother-in-law is around, you might find you start to like her more as she jumps in to relieve you of some of the burdens and extra responsibilities around the house. A little praise sprinkled there might do quite a lot. We didn't live far from my partner's family, and I know they were helping out in ways I was oblivious to during the whole experience. I eventually learned more about that the second time around the carousel.

The infamous phrase "We are pregnant!" is not so much a statement of fact in the physical sense, but it is a declaration of your mutual commitment to creating a child as a couple. You won't be peeing umpteen extra times a day, and you won't get constipation and haveyour organs squish while you outgrow the shoe collection you bought as an adult, thinking that was the one size on you that could never change. But you can absorb some of the extra burdens and try to enjoy giving her downtime genuinely.

Show Her You Care by Educating Yourself

At some point, you will want to attend some birthing classes with your companion to learn more about your roles and some general idea of what you should expect. Don't ever get the idea that those classes prepare you for what's to come. They are something you do together, so it is an excellent show of commitment — just like accompanying her to doctor appointments. Showing her support in simple gestures lets her know you are in it together.

An even more impressive way to show your partner that you mean to be an active participant is to read about pregnancy. Instead of watching movies about the Darwin Awards for people who died in dumb ways or TikTok compilations that leave you in good humor but scratching your head, use that video time to man up by dedicating time to studying pregnancy and birth. This sacrifice of replacing something useless for something useful will serve a purpose when you mention a topic you'd like to know her opinion about and when you tell her what you learned about pregnancy.

Planning

In later chapters, we will learn what happens in four of the three trimesters. Yeah, that there are four trimesters is not a typo. Just because the baby is crying, that doesn't mean the game is over. The goal we are looking at here is to create a comprehensive plan for the expectant couple.

To be an effective partner in the pregnancy, it is wise to take on a planning role. It will force you to do some research into the realities of pregnancy and birth, learn about all the things you don't expect, and will help you feel reassured when the water breaks and it is showtime. Initiating the planning is not so much taking charge as building out your parental resume. You will take on your responsibilities in the role but share the planning with your partner. This also helps with communications and feeling out the expectations of each participant in the parental team. That makes sure the event is one you participate in like a partner and not like a wide-eyed lemur shocked into a frozen state by the rage of the machine.

Some of the most demanding aspects of planning for the long haul are budgeting and the birthing plan.

Budgeting. Beyond bathing in pee and potentially becoming intimate with parts of your partner's anatomy that even she will never see, discovering the actual cost of bringing a new member into the family can be the most surprising part of the pregnancy adventure. It is never too soon to start thinking about finances, even well before you think about having a baby. If you haven't thought about finances, the surprise, amazement, and wonder of learning that you have been involved in the creation of life can be supplanted by substantial sticker shock. Following this general mapping, budgeting includes considerations for:

* Wardrobe augmentation
* The baby room
* Baby care
* Time off work

* Medical costs

Some of these concerns may be offset by gifts from friends and family or work benefits but failing to consider any one of them may end up as part of a costly surprise. Failing to face the reality of which direction your life savings may be headed can only add to the stress of the situation and ultimately end in something resembling disaster. A financial disaster can be avoided by careful planning, putting aside money over time, and taking a good look at the benefits that your employer does or does not provide. Depending on where you live, various government benefits may also be available. New parents who are dedicated to making the most of enjoying their first baby can accomplish miraculous things even on such a short runway.

Wardrobe augmentation. Mama is going to outgrow practically everything during her pregnancy but her scarves. The rate of change won't be exactly constant, and the rate of growth due to the size of the fetus and genetics and eating habits of the mom will vary widely. Glamour is usually not the goal. Comfort, breathability, and practicality are more likely interests. Forbes says the average mom spends less than $1000 on maternity clothing. This relatively low number is expected because of the short-term length of wear, sharing between friends, and availability of low-cost maternity clothing options. Unless a mama plans to build her own army one soldier at a time, some garments may get no more than a few days of wear before they are retired. It is good to try and think of practical value rather than a radical fashion show.

The baby room. Even if there is a stand-alone room for the new arrival, a special place built just for the child can be advantageous. Nap times for the baby in a room behind her own door can be peaceful siestas with no interruption. Fitting the room with a crib and a separate changing table or chest of drawers does not have to cost a fortune. A practical matching grouping can be purchased anywhere between $200 to $1000 with a conservative budget. Be sure to check the safety ratings for any product that you buy using a platform that rates products publicly. It is never worth a few dollars saved to put your precious child at risk of harm. Keep in mind that these items may only be in use for a relatively short time and saving costs on the nursery to buy furniture to last the child through their teens is probably the wiser investment. A baby monitor is an inexpensive piece of added insurance against a baby's distress but can also be a soothing unobtrusive way to listen to precious sleeping breaths and cooing as children wake from a peaceful slumber. It makes up for the stresses of the inevitable crying.

Baby care. Baby care includes such things as formula, diapers, baby clothes, toys & teething, car seat, travel/diaper pack, stroller, carrier, nap seat, high chair. What you choose to get depends on what is important to you and your lifestyle, but all of this should be planned and purchased well before the trip to the hospital. Your choices matter. For example, reusable cloth diapers using a service and disposables can cost about the same price ($1000/year), but they have a different impact on the environment—research product ratings for anything you plan to buy with special attention to safety. Wood finishes on toys can be particularly deceptive as they may make things look dandy but could have long-term effects on a child's development. Chemicals and lead in a baby's diet are a no-no, and they will not discriminate as to what can and should go in their mouths. Keep all kitty litter out of reach of children, use safety devices on electrical sockets, and baby-gate everything that can't be child-proofed.

Time off work. Maternity and paternity leave are benefits some people get to enjoy depending on their employment and employer policies. For a fledgling parental duo, this one benefit may be a strategic reason for choosing one job over another when entering the child-rearing age. No doubt, parents with these benefits will want to take advantage of them. However, not everyone has this luxury, and when they do, the benefits vary widely between paid and unpaid time allowed. The key here is to be aware of any compensation that needs to be accounted for during any period that either or both parents will go without pay. It is good to plan for emergency time in case mom needs to take it lightly as her full-term approaches. Suppose the mother will not be returning to work for an extended period. In that case, the double whammy strikes where you have to account both for the lack of her financial contribution and the fact that baby raises household costs and lowers the limbo bar you have to squeeze under.

Medical costs. One of the unavoidable expenditures of pregnancy is medical costs. It could be argued that it starts with the pregnancy test and essentially never ends until the child is supporting him or herself. But the practical and immediate expenses of the nine months of pregnancy and subsequent birth are what is addressed here. There will be regular checkups with an obstetrician (the doctor specifically concerned with pregnancy and childbirth), tests (ultrasounds and laboratory tests), and the hospital bill, which can range widely between hospitals and methods of birth.

Without medical benefits, the cost of attended natural childbirth can be between $10,000 and $20,000. A C-section (where the child is extracted by an incision in the abdomen) can be up to $50,000. Things such as induction (artificially inducing labor) and epidurals (a medical procedure that taps anesthetic into an area of the spinal cord to numb the pain of the mother giving birth) cost more. Financially, it may be best to call a taxi after the water breaks and hope the birth occurs in transit. Due to the additional risks, that is not something you should pray for.

Ultimately, the cost of having a baby with traditional care if you have no benefits is somewhere around the same price as an inexpensive state university degree in the United States. If you have no insurance, had done no planning for the pregnancy, and it was unexpected, chances are you will need some type of social assistance or to take out loans that you will be paying off till right about when your 'baby' will be going off to college. Those are a lot of dollar signs to confront, and that is why it is a good idea to make plans before being surprised.

With benefits or other assistance, the costs drop dramatically, but studies suggest the average cost of childbirth, even with insurance, is about $5000. That can still be a significant sum to plan for, depending on your financial status. For other people, it may be the amount they spend monthly for online gaming fees. Now maybe the time to consider whether you could give up a non-essential expense to put toward your savings.

The point here is to make a financial plan. It may start by putting away a certain number of dollars from your weekly paycheck and should involve research into benefits and government support. List out everything you absolutely need, research the costs through your doctor and hospitals, and know what the total investment will be. At that point, you can make an informed decision as to how to cover the expense without loading up interminable debt.

Your Birthing Plan. While some experts consider 'budgeting' as part of the birthing plan, it seems to me to be too large in scope to squeeze in comfortably. The birthing plan is really just an outline of what you would like to think will happen during the birth and making some strategic notes about stuff you will not want to have to think of while they are happening. When the waters break, that is not the time to start looking for the keys or packing for the trip to the hospital. You want all of that done weeks and even months in advance.

The plan should contain a lot of boring-but-necessary stuff that will expedite everything. You don't necessarily need to include where the keys are, but you will want to be sure to develop a habit of hanging them on a hook by the door. This is one of several things that are in the plan but remain unwritten. If you won't be driving and need or want to use a taxi, make sure they respond rapidly and include their phone number on the plan.

The written plan. Things you want to write into the plan include:

* Names and phone numbers of doctors and the hospital (and get these on speed dial on your phone).
* The schedule of doctors and appointment dates.
* The expected date of birth.
* Special concerns and considerations.

I doubt that I could have stated that last bullet point in a way that was any more vague. That is because the topic is vague. It will really have to do with the preferences of the mom for the birth environment and how the process should evolve. Listing preferences for music and available comfort foods may not be a bad idea, although that should be taken care of with the hospital bag (which we'll get to in a moment). More important things are preferences for epidural, natural childbirth, use of forceps, and birth location (at home, hospital, birthing pool, or taxi). A lot of this falls into the hands of the mother. Some may be decisions made by the couple as a team, such as baby names and circumcision preferences. This should pretty much include everything the mother can't contribute rationally while consumed by the pain of childbirth, and the father may not be conscious of doing having passed out from the things he did not expect to see. In other words, in an emergency where neither parent is capable, an attending nurse should be able to grab the page and locate everything she needs to know.

The unwritten plan. The unwritten daddy parts of the program include very practical things. No one will be worried about you because you are not carrying the package that needs to be delivered, but you have to be the tactical engineer.

* Know your job. If you are going to be in the room during the birth, be there and do what is expected of you. Make sure first that your partner wants you there for her support.
* Scope out the hospital. Take a hospital tour long before the time comes. Know where the admissions area is, where you can park long-term (all birthing episodes are not short), where the birthing rooms are (floor, desk, and arrangement), know where you can take breaks, locate something to eat, and where you might find a bathroom.
* Know direct and alternative routes to drive. Get to know the area and roads between your home and the hospital. If some freak backup happens, you do not want to get caught in it while rushing to the hospital (unless you are hoping for that taxi birth).
* Add your stuff to a hospital bag. Don't expect your partner to pack for you. Be ready to go at the first sign of contractions.

The Hospital Bag. It is best to pack a hospital bag and have them ready well ahead of the date the birth is expected. Even a 'normal' term can sometimes be shorter than expected. It is a good idea to have separate bags because the mom may need additional things. She won't necessarily be leaving the hospital right away. Separating the bags leads to less confusion when looking for things and allows each party of the duo to manage their own perceived needs.

You may want more or less than this, but here are some things to consider.

* Phone chargers
* Cash
* Entertainment
* Extension cord
* Change of clothes
* Toothbrush
* Deodorant
* Tissues or hand-wipes

Don't Neglect Yourself Entirely.

This process is going to be stressful and rewarding. You may actually come out the other side as a better person because you are forced to develop all sorts of empathetic tools. You will undoubtedly become more capable as a partner because you have to be responsive to your partner's needs and may have gained new abilities. You will be better prepared to be a dad because you have been building skills by just thinking about your family and the future.

While you have these improvements in yourself as a take-away, you'll still need to have some time out from the pressure of responsibilities. Be gentle in approaching this and also consider that you may be taking a break, but your significant other never gets one. Taking some time out to meet with your friends to go bowling or out for a run. Maybe you can break away for a sporting event. Whatever your interests and preferences are for taking a break, consider them well, keep them responsible, and make them short. If possible, take these breaks with some members of the daddy pool so you can multitask. Sharing your experience with those in similar circumstances can provide insight and comfort. Do not go back home smelling of anything. Many pregnant women become highly sensitive to smell. Beer on your breath, wisps of the scent of a shared cigarette, and the stale odor of a bar will not be the best way to arrive home. Need I say that it is a bad time to visit a perfume shop, even if the gift is for her.

Be sure the time you will be spending out is covered by family or friends visiting with your partner. Do not leave her alone, especially later in the pregnancy. Allow your time of respite to be hers as well. A little time away from each other will help make invisible reparations even if things are going well.

Parenting and Partnering Power

This chapter presents many things to think about in the coming months, but empathy, communication, and budgeting should be things you engage first. These critical beginnings set the tone for a long time to come.

Get yourself a daddy notebook. In it, leave a page or two at the beginning to brainstorm ideas about what you need to include in your budgeting or just to doodle. Don't think of it as a chore, and make it your own. The more fun you have with it, the more you will use it.

The importance of writing out a budget and seeing how to meet it realistically can not be understated. Believe it or not, people do actually start saving for parenthood before they even know they are expecting. When you think it is time to start writing out budget considerations, give yourself ten pages or so to allow for expansion, changing your mind, and revisions. You want to leave room to revise in every section. You are not etching stone, so put the chisels aside. If you write with a pencil rather than a pen, your daddy notebook becomes a sort of whiteboard. With every section you create, consider making tabs with Post-its, so they are easy to find.

Make a section to collect things you need to discuss with your partner and use the pages to think of the best way to approach subjects that may be sensitive. Allow yourself to explore your ideas and feelings and make an effort to find ways to be communicative. If you are comfortable sharing the book, that's great, but you can also keep it as a journal, under lock and key.

Practice empathy and humility whenever you get the chance, and grade yourself on the response. If you reacted badly to something, write it down and think about how you could have done better. In baseball, hitters have good and bad at-bats. The best players learn from both. If you work on being sensitive to how your partner feels, you will get better at it, and your personal explorations will become a productivity tool for your relationship.

Chapter Two:

The 1st Trimester -
Months 1 to 3+
(Weeks 0 to 14) of Pregnancy

Most people think of pregnancy as being nine months long. The gestation period for a baby is 40 weeks on average or about 280 days. That breaks not so neatly into trimesters of 14, 13, and 13 weeks each. The odd week has to fall somewhere. A good reason to think of the first trimester as the trimester with the flex week is that counting the start date of the pregnancy is not always very precise. Doctors usually mark the beginning of the pregnancy from the last date of menstruation. That isn't really very accurate in many ways, not the least of which is that conception will generally happen two weeks later.

When the page turns from "We're trying" to "We're expecting," it seems like that should come with a new attitude. Out of the gate, that attitude might be one of surprise and anticipation. There may be a spot on the roster for any feeling from the whole gamut of human emotion, fear, panic, giddiness, confusion, elation, joy, and the seemingly irrational syndrome called couvade (see the *What is Couvade?* Sidebar). Whatever the case, there is no prescription for your feelings, and there is no real prescription for her physical state.

Both of you will experience a change in one form or another, and working together to master the obstacle course is always a better choice than feeling like your partner should just buck up and deal with it. Life got more complicated with your willing participation, and it is a time to step up rather than flounder. It is actually quite likely that the challenges will do more to make you rise to the occasion and get better at being a husband and father.

What is Couvade?

Couvade is a sort of sympathetic state where men develop symptoms that are normal for a pregnant female to experience in reaction to their partner's pregnancy. This may include such things as backaches, cramps, dental conditions, nausea, and weight gain. All of this comes as an addition to your personal emotional roller-coaster, exhaustion, and consternation.

Some might argue it is purely psychological (psychosomatic), while others say it is due to actual physical changes that arise from extreme empathy and changes in the hormonal atmosphere of your environment (pheromones). In the latter case, chemicals that become plentiful in the air affect the natural balance of a man's constitution. That means the syndrome might be something like the McClintock effect, where women of child-bearing age sync menstrual cycles when they are in close proximity over a period of time.

Enough men (about 30% on average) experience the syndrome that is worthy as a subject of study. Even though I never had the experience of couvade myself, I'm still not one to poo-poo the possibility just because it didn't happen to me. It might be that I failed to be more emotionally in tune with my spouse or that I was not a good receptor for the other potential causes. If it were an emotional failing, that might be even worse than suffering the condition. At the time you would experience the condition is the same time that your spouse needs your emotional support and empathy the most. Because that is the case, try your best not to overplay your reactions.

To be a successful husband, partner, and father, you need a good understanding of the changes occurring with your partner, the baby, and how it is best for you to do what you can to meet the challenges posed by this partnership and be a champion.

Rising to the Challenge

The fragility of the early stages of pregnancy is nothing to ignore. It is a time when the fetus is most vulnerable, key developments are occurring, and interruption in the process could create complications. You have to be both the man of the house, sympathetic partner, and hall monitor to keep up with your end of the bargain. While you may already do manly things that require masculine strength, it is best to remain aware of what you can do to keep your partner rested and happy. Going out of your way to treat her a little like royalty will not go unnoticed. Special attention to small things, like not having to be told to take out the garbage while her sense of smell is overly keen, can keep her anxiety levels low and actually affect fetal development. Taking the helm on tasks you don't always engage in or initiate is part of assuming your new role.

If you didn't before, you now own all kinds of lifting, from grocery bags to dinner plates. If it has been since the early days of dating that you opened the car door for your partner, make it a practice again. Keep active, and you might just ward off some of the pounds you might put on when you become your partner's snack-mate. You get a double-whammy as the levels of stress increase, spiking your cortisol levels, which affects fat and carbohydrate metabolism. Don't do so much that you leap up every time she starts to speak, but remain conscious of those moments where you can relieve her of burdens. She will have enough to deal with during hormonal and other bodily changes, which only pile on top of her own concerns.

Be sympathetic to your partner by supporting her emotionally. If either of you smoked, now is a good time to quit. If you would like to share a bottle of wine with dinner, it is a good time for you to give that up when she does. It is also a time to start supporting each other's healthy habits. Getting outside together for a walk instead of one more hour on the couch watching Netflix can help set a precedent and nurture something the two of you and the child will benefit from.

The support you show her goes well beyond skipping a glass of wine. Certain foods are known to have a potentially higher risk factor in causing complications during pregnancy. Some of these foods are actually things that are ordinarily considered healthy when consumed outside of that 40-week window. If you had a sushi date night every week before the pregnancy, time to cut that out or be very selective in choosing only those delicacies that are fully cooked. Nothing resembling a raw egg, under-cooked meat, and cold cuts, or risky raw vegetables (e.g., bean sprouts) is allowed past the lips of the expectant mother. Cuts of large fish in any amount (e.g., tuna and swordfish) are not good choices because of the potential mercury content. Caffeine in moderation is acceptable but not recommended. Supplements of any sort should be brought to the attention of your doctor. Even vitamins can contain high doses of particular components, which are known to increase the risk of birth defects (e.g., vitamin A).

Potential dangers do not only lie within the mother's diet. While the baby can be pretty resilient in the protective cavity where it is encased, other environmental factors can play into the threats in a world it has not yet entered. Everything that comes in contact with the mother needs to be scrutinized because even seemingly harmless situations may bring about complications. If some of the mother's hobbies include woodworking, painting, and refinishing projects, fumes from the products she uses can be hazardous to the unborn, even in ventilated areas. Salves may sometimes have additives that can be absorbed through the skin. Favorite herbal teas may include ingredients that are not recommended during pregnancy for various reasons. Calming hot baths or saunas may raise body temperature to unsafe levels for the fetus. Anything that may cause jarring that tears the placenta, like car accidents, falls, or amusement park rides, are all things that should be avoided. For goodness sake, keep her hands out of the kitty litter and wash yours if you come into contact. Hair coloring and getting nails done is never as important as the health of the fetus. If she has allergic reactions that can only be traced to the bathroom, have an expert check for mold and mildew and take care of those infestations. The key here is to be cautious, sensible, and aware rather than afraid.

In all, the mother's body needs a higher level of nutrition during pregnancy, and the best way to achieve that is with healthy, nutrient-rich whole foods. That means this will not really be a pizza and Cheetos festival. Cravings are a thing, and there may likely be strange combinations of foods, and the pantry might get over-stocked with snackaroos of all sorts when mom has a hunger-driven binge-buy. It may be unlikely and possibly even cruel to keep a pregnant woman on an exceedingly strict diet (although that will sometimes be necessary for particular conditions), but an ounce of willpower may mean a lifetime of difference for a child. For best results, take cooking into your own hands, build menus that reflect her food preferences as they change, and err on the side of caution. You are being conscious of you and your significant other, but you are feeding the engine running on the peanut sprouting inside of her.

If you adopt a plan to rise to the challenge, it may be an opportunity not only to strengthen your partnership but to build a better, healthier lifestyle, embrace responsibilities, and work at the core of improving the prospects of your family before it even technically manifests in the cries of the birthing room.

Stress and the Pregnant Father

This subtitle isn't entirely accurate as you are not physically carrying the baby, but you are carrying a significant portion of the burden. Unless you are a zen master already, there are moments where stresses will forsake you. If you are feeling empathetic, present symptoms of couvade, and catch yourself in fits of anger or moodiness, you have likely come to a point where you should practice behavior modifications to help control your state of mind. If you don't do something early on, the effects could bleed over into your performance at work, affect your sleep patterns and pitch you into an avoidable downward spiral at home.

Don't get this wrong. As stated in the opening chapter, stress is a performance enhancer. It provides motivation to encourage taking action. If you go about this the right way, you will be learning skills that can help you cope with all types of stressful situations over the long haul. Things like retaining calm during your toddler's temper tantrums while out shopping will be easier to handle, you'll be more metered in your response, and ultimately you will be a better parent all-around.

There are many ways to practice the art of composure by taking simple measures. Saying "I need a drink" isn't one of them. The goal is to be mindful of your stress levels and build practices into your everyday life that make maintaining your cool second nature. When you practice and master techniques for keeping a cool head, you can free yourself from medications, become more cognizant and efficient, and simply brush away the demons before they can possess you. If you develop several tools, you should be able to practice it anywhere to quell everything from road rage to panic attacks. Some tools you might begin to practice with are:

* Breathing
* Meditation
* Self Hypnosis

Breathing. By far, the most practical and easiest way to gain control of heightened levels of stress is breathing. The best thing about it is that lungs are something you always have with you and the process of inhaling and exhaling is something you have to do anyway. You don't even have to take extra time for it.

Because you do it from the moment you are born, you'd think that everyone on earth would pretty much be an expert at breathing. Such is not at all the case. There are better and worse ways to breathe. In fact, if you go about it wrong, you actually enhance your propensity to become anxious. Short, shallow breathing is akin to hyperventilation, but they are not at all the same. The difference is that hyperventilation is quick, deep breathing. Shallow breathing deprives the respiratory system of oxygen. Either are poorly regulated respiration and cause a stressful imbalance in the blood oxygen level that the body will react to over time.

At its simplest, breathing methods range from just consciously focusing on the rhythm of your breathing to advanced techniques like Wim Hof's breathing methods or various breathing exercises (e.g., lookup 4-7-8, 7/11, and 4-4-4 breathing techniques). The timed methods just suggest the duration of inhaling, holding your breath, and exhaling. No matter which plans you choose to practice, practicing is the key to getting it right and having the method as your companion. Whatever you choose, do not push yourself with it to the point of discomfort. It is an exercise and not a weight-lifting regimen.

The common features of any breathing exercise are practicing breathing through your nose, breathing with your diaphragm rather than your rib cage, and controlling the pace of your breathing. Breathing with your mouth open bypasses an integral part of your breathing apparatus that helps filter allergens, dust, and germs. It helps to humidify the air as it passes through the nasal cavities and helps to avoid having a dry mouth or throat, which can lead to an enhanced risk of infections.

Breathing with the diaphragm helps you bring oxygen deep into the lungs. It helps in exhaling higher percentages of carbon dioxide while enhancing the efficient uptake of oxygen. People who take shallow breaths do not make the most of respiration, which can add to fatigue and other metabolic issues.

Make it a habit to breathe correctly and be mindful in times where you are not really able to do anything else. When sitting in traffic, in an elevator, in a line at a checkout, and any moment where you find yourself just waiting, take a deep breath or several. No one will be looking at you strangely for breathing. Eventually, you will do it automatically, and you will naturally develop a stronger sense of calm.

Meditation. Never thought you'd meditate? Time to give in and never say never. Meditation is probably one of the most well-known ways to achieve a sense of calm. Contrary to popular opinion, it is not necessarily spiritual, strange, or exotic. It doesn't require special tools or poses. At its best, it is absolutely the easiest thing that you can ever do for your well-being. Forget the incense and lotus position unless you like them. Meditation is a lot like a slightly more formal version of concentrating on your breathing. The most significant difference between meditation and breathing is that you will generally try to set aside a little time in the day specifically to practice meditation. Whether you choose to implement a mantra or simply breathe and allow your muscles to relax, daily practice of the ritual can yield benefits that last all day.

What you do during meditation is often said to be clearing your mind of thoughts. While that might be a goal for some, it should not be the only goal — if it is a goal at all. Thoughts will happen during meditation, just like dreams emerge during sleep. While meditating, you will try to let any thoughts leave as quickly as they emerged by not indulging them — especially if they are troubling. If you can learn to allow thoughts to pass, you can learn to let go of annoyances just as easily and stay on a more even keel.

Meditation, unlike breathing, is not automatic. It is something you practice and learn, and you will get better at it the longer you work at it. The totality of the subject is really the source for another book, but a lot of methods exist. Progressive relaxation (i.e., concentrating on specific muscle groups to release tension), guided meditation (i.e., following a guide's suggestions such as on a Youtube video), active meditation (i.e., moving in forms like Yoga, Qigong, or even walking), or visualization (i.e., picturing tranquil scenery or evoking calming emotions) are varied practices which may resonate with you. Try them all, pick what suits you best, and do yourself a favor and practice every day. Even if you only get in a few minutes, learning to control emotional bursts will help steady your response to triggers and curb the immediacy of your reactions.

Self-Hypnosis. It can be argued that there is really very little difference between meditation and self-hypnosis except that the reluctance factors differ. Some people don't like the idea of meditation because it appears too spiritual. Self-hypnosis gets branded by the misunderstanding that entering into a trance-like state allows other people to control your thoughts. In both cases, the preconceptions are untrue. While the consensus seems to be that self-hypnosis is different because you cross into a mind state that leaves you open to subliminal suggestions, those suggestions are meditations of your own. Self-hypnosis seeks an endpoint and a specific goal (e.g., reducing or eliminating bad habits), while meditation is geared toward absently experiencing the moment.

There is a lot of overlap between the two practices, and some people might prefer one over the other simply in name. In the end, the goal is to reach for an enhanced version of yourself so that you are a better you, a better partner, and a more effective guide in helping to nurture and raise your children. Take a look on Youtube for guided self-hypnosis sessions and try out the myriad of different styles which mimic the models of meditation.

Which Way Did My Friends Go?

There is nothing worse than a one-dimensional dad. Imagine growing up in the shadow of a cardboard cutout that really has no personality, interests, or passions. You'd just have a button to press to have money fall out of its pockets. The smile would be permanent and unwavering. It is a practical idea if you want your perfect family to be a Photoshopped wall-hanging.

The thing that a cardboard dad doesn't work with is emotional development. In a study that would be impossible to replicate with humans, psychologist Harry Harlow created a situation where rhesus monkeys were taken from their mothers within hours of birth. The mother was replaced with two surrogates, one that was a cloth-covered wire-frame that supplied nothing else and a wire-frame that was equipped to bottle feed. The study showed that the monkeys preferred the soft, comforting version of their mother to the one that simply provided food. Further studies in this area led to changes in how children were treated at orphanages, social services, and childcare.

The take-away point here is that if you are a cardboard cutout, your child will someday realize that there is little beyond the image. Instead of striving to be that perfect cardboard cutout, you will be most helpful and effective in raising your children if you actually have dimension in the form of interests, personality, and drive. This is where friends, hobbies, and adventure become inseparable from your value as a parent. Your genuine passion for a hobby, ability to interact with friends in a healthy way, and work on developing interests help nurture you. This, in turn, enables you to nurture your child. It also gives you and your partner a break from one another that probably leads to a more healthy appreciation of your relationship.

You can't just pause all aspects of your life because of pregnancy and hope to learn and grow as a person. Indeed, it is imperative to be heavily involved in and educated about the adventure your family has embarked on. Still, it is claustrophobic and deadening to make that the only source of stimulation in your life. You won't be good at turning off all your friendships and interests just to try to turn them back on when the time seems more convenient. You may have less time to dedicate, but don't let friends, hobbies, and interests fall off the map while you turn to cardboard.

The richer you allow your life experiences to be, the more you can share in your children's growth and their exploration as they move through life.

Immersing Yourself in Understanding Trimester #1

Knowing what the first third of the pregnancy holds in store for you, mother and fetus will make the whole experience of the events easier. I am absolutely sure that my participation the first time around was sub-par because I expected that what I needed to know would come to me. Instead, it likely was more of a case of: "Pfft. Nevermind. It takes longer to explain it." If you really want to be an asset in your partnership — and you should — learn about:

 * What is happening with the baby?
 * What's happening with your partner?
 * How can you best be of help?

What Is Happening with the Baby? In the first weeks of pregnancy, the baby is just starting to form, and by the end of the first month is still about the size of a grain of rice. While more features begin to emerge over the coming weeks, they are hardly recognizable. Even by the end of the second month, if you were to see the fetus, it would look more like some sort of prehistoric animal (or alien) than anything human. Four weeks more into the maturing miracle, the fetus is only about an inch long. It has managed to nurture more changes in your partner's physiology than its own.

Almost like the magic of a lump of clay becoming a beautiful creation in the hands of an artisan, the fetus looks far more human by the end of the trimester. The baby is still tiny and quite fragile. Even at that small size, the baby is essentially fully formed, although in miniature. The little fingers and toes begin to grow nails, and small movements begin in the extremities and jaw. While there is still not much size and mass, it is about three inches long and right about an ounce. For dads, let's say about the size of a strangely shaped baseball—the risk of any complications that have not already been identified drops significantly. Because the 14th week is recognized with the decrease in risk, it is often the milestone where couples choose to reveal the little miracle.

However, do not ignore that complications can still arise if you let your guard down. There is still no room for working with hazardous chemicals and cleaning products. Eating safely and paying attention to everything the mother encounters is critical to the fetus' further development.

What Is Happening to Your Partner? The sudden and grotesque emergence of hormones in the pregnant mother is nothing short of volcanic and chaotic. Even women who have proven throughout a relationship to be relatively stable troopers during the trials and tribulations of menstrual cycles may suddenly find their bane in the surge of blossoming motherhood. Picking a daisy may cause uncontrollable weeping. Swooning from nausea may lead to the inability to get out of bed with only the comfort of a vomit bowl and Saltines in close reach. Smells like the cologne she bought you for Christmas may lead to hissing reminders to take a shower. Mind you, she picked the scent, and she now rages at it in a passion.

There will be no respite from the primordial response, and she can't take a pill to fix it without endangering the whole reason for the presence of the onslaught. The father might well be tempted to consider a vacation to a foreign land just for a short 14 weeks or so, but the truth is that this is when you may be needed the most. Getting screamed at in the birthing room is nothing compared to the potential tempest that threatens to cleave oceans in two and scatter the broken hulls of boats on the rocks. But the waves of turmoil can ease just as quickly to sad moments and calm. Changes in blood flow cause discomfort in the form of constipation and swelling of the breasts. It may be best to designate a particular bathroom off-limits to anyone but the mother if you have the luxury of more than one. The growing frequency of peeing increases in concert with nausea, and the whole makes having a b-line to the facilities all but essential.

What I described here is the worst-case scenario. Some women go through the first 14 weeks with barely any symptoms at all. Your spouse is experiencing a chemical cocktail as she has never had before. Just as patients respond differently to various medications, the result comes down to an individual's experience with their change. You might experience every bit of the horror, or barely any at all.

The question left to ask is: what is a father to do?

How Can You Best Be of Help? There is probably little that is more stressful than being helpless. In various animal studies in laboratory settings, animals are put into situations that seemingly can not be resolved. In these situations, the animals invariably surrender and accept fate. But this should not be the course of action for the educated and empowered modern male. Knowledge is your advantage, and sympathetic action is your key to success. You can't take the struggles from her, but you can be smart about the steps you take to ease her discomforts.

The first thing to do is to deal with your own problems. You are a better partner immediately if you are not bringing issues to her when she is under siege by her own body. While you want to commiserate with your partner in moments when she seems to be in the mood, do what you need to do to take care of your mental attitude. Do not express your suffering to her, and do not complain about how she is failing to handle her torments. Look back at the section on "Stress and the Pregnant Father" and start indulging your exploration into an embodiment of tranquility.

Notice her trends for her. She may not see that the cup of coffee she allows herself in the morning encourages the rise of magma at her core. Likewise, some activities, foods, or beverages might provide an umbrella of calm. If you have taken the advice from early on, keep notes to track her successes and outbursts and what seems to be a trigger. A resolution may come down to something simple and easy to control.

Consider yourself officially responsible for everything. When she feels up to it, she will possibly push you out of the way and take over certain things, especially close to the end of the first trimester. Just don't count on it. You should still never let her exertions be extreme, and anything involving more than hand soap is likely not something you want her getting involved in cleaning. Do not make her feel parasitic and lazy. Reassure her that you are doing what you can, and it is the least you can do to participate in your joint venture.

Romance like food can take on whole new directions. Cravings for either can emerge and wane. Try your very best to be supportive and flexible when satiating appetites or resist making ill-timed advances. Stay on call as the concierge and make your mission to serve. Both food and changes due to pregnancy will have effects on her physique. She may not feel attractive. Assure her that your attraction to her is not changing and maybe let on that you think she is beautiful.

Show some interest in the progression of the process. You might want to have a camera-ready (or at least your phone) to capture and share memories occurring during the pregnancy. Consider introducing a joint project like a baby book or maybe a modest web page to keep family and friends informed of the progress. Showing her that you care about this being something you have engaged in together may help quell her anxieties, doubts and shorten the swing in the pendulum of her moods.

When all else fails, it is time to listen and listen well. She won't always tell you what she is thinking exactly, and she may not be able to. You have to finally be the mind-reader she has always envisioned her prince charming would become, and you have no other part in the movie for now. She is handling the physical burden. She will get the attention. You will be more than a pack mule, but you might often feel like one. Beyond that tortured exterior, she is still your partner. She may not be mindful enough to have any regrets about outbursts and moodiness, and you should not expect her to. If you read this carefully enough, you know what's coming. With the right attitude, you might even enjoy it.

Come to terms with the fact that the hormonal changes in your partner are temporary. She will start shedding the masks of all her new personalities as the tide of hormones recedes. Assure her that you are aware but do it in very gentle ways. You are not in a good spot if in the middle of a tirade you blurt out, "I know that is the hormones speaking." As you turn your head away from her reception of the comment, something handy like a lamp may be headed toward your skull. You can probably depend on the cord being short enough to keep you from harm, but never underestimate the newborn athletic prowess of a woman in the throws of chemical change.

She may be terrified by the whole process and what she sees as an insurmountable mountain of trying to push a bowling ball through the eye of a needle. If you can clear the first 14 weeks without incident and lunge for the finish line, just know that there are only 26 weeks left to go. You will likely break your silence to friends by this point, and the marker for the second trimester can begin. Things might just get a little easier from here on out.

Parenting and Partnering Power

Now is your time to start building rituals. Some of these might only last through pregnancy, but all can be helpful, and some can improve the quality of life for your whole family for the long haul. You want to focus on being the hall monitor for anything that your partner does that she may forget could cause risk to the baby. You need to be gentle and empathetic about your approach. That doesn't mean setting up spy cams or flying drones around to follow every step she takes — unless it is a joke, and you know you won't scare her to death. Never scold your companion. That is a partner you are talking to, and you need to treat her like one.

Being alert and mindful goes hand-in-hand with tending to your own needs and building skills for controlling your emotions. Choose a method of dealing with stress and begin working with it immediately. It may help to start a section in your notebook to keep track of your exercise and make notes to yourself about what you are doing right. Learn from the mistakes, but don't be shy about noticing you improve.

Chapter Three:

The 2nd Trimester - Months 3 to 6
(Weeks 15 to 27) of Pregnancy

If the first trimester felt like anything less than running a marathon, consider yourself lucky. No matter how well prepared you thought you were (even if you read this book before it happened), you probably, on one occasion at least, found yourself experiencing a feeling akin to being blindfolded on a diving board off the side of a pirate ship. If you've come out the other side without anyone having to yell "Man overboard!" you are a champion. There is hope on the horizon. It may be time to take the blindfold off, taunt the sharks swimming in the waters below you, and step back on the ship. Not to promise anything because the unexpected can happen, and the effects of the first trimester can go extra innings. Still, something should be emerging; you should both be coming to terms with the 'routine' of being a couple that is expecting. That alone is a triumph.

You have probably developed some habits as to how to handle your new responsibilities in practice — which is the real reason reading alone doesn't make you prepared. If you've ever thought about going sky diving, you read about it to prepare, you took a class and read a book, and you knew everything about it, you wouldn't have to jump out of the plane. It is probably the one thing that root canal and having sex have in common: If you have never done it, all the preparation only gives you an idea of what to expect. When Dr Smiley says, "you are going to feel a little pinch," and the needle sliding into your gum-line seems to be the length of a samurai sword you have arrived.

The familiarity means you and your partner will both begin to experience less stress, whether or not the actual situation has improved. The period where you can both begin to enjoy the honeymoon period has arrived. If you opened up and announced the pregnancy at this juncture, you will be able to speak with people around you and share experiences and emotions you may have been hiding. You'll feel a little like you are emerging from a cocoon and experience the release of telling someone a secret you have been withholding — and that's because it is precisely what you were doing. By no means is this the end. You've only done three laps in this marathon, and there are six more to go. But just like a runner in a race, you've settled into a position in the field. You don't want to look behind, but you do want to look ahead to see where you will end up in this race and strategize as to how to make the best effort in greeting the finish line.

First things first. Take a look back at the things you didn't manage to accomplish in the first trimester and replicate them on to your to-do list for the second. It would help if you hadn't procrastinated, but you still have time to make up for it. Note down all the positive things you think you did and get ready to keep replicating those actions; focus on further developing the skills you see as benefiting your relationship and your family's future. You've got the battle scars, and should you have the luck to go through that experience again, it will indeed seem familiar, easier, and welcome.

We have an Announcement!

Before you rush out in traffic on your horse galloping through the streets yelling the news of the confirmed pregnancy to anyone who will listen, take a moment to plan. Passing the receptionist desk at work and flipping on the intercom to announce the new arrival is probably not the best way to go to work. The announcement that you

46

and your partner are expecting should trickle down through the proper channels lest it runs upstream in a way that isn't natural.

Take every step to make sure those who will be hurt most by hearing second-hand news hear it first from you. Your boss goes before any of your buddies at work. Your parents go before a Facebook post. Having the sense to treat your allies with the respect they deserve will only help strengthen those bonds that you might just need as your experience continues and your need to rely on support expands.

The gesture of going boss-first drives home the implication that you respect that he/she will be affected by the potential shifts in your workload and days that need to be covered. It also speaks to the idea that you take your job very seriously. Asking for advice about how he/she prefers things to be handled also plays a political chip. Any time you ask someone for their advice, it creates an alliance.

Friends and family who already know when you take to social media will be likely to voice their support and help to be sure the word gets around to the corners of your social imprint. This will take some of the burden off you for alerting everyone you know, and you don't show up some months later to a party with a baby bump whose origin is suspicious to the host.

The announcement is another thrilling step, but good sense uses that to your advantage. Already your child is paying dividends.

Finances: Exploring Your Resources

If you have not yet taken the initiative to explore the potential benefits you can take advantage of, now is the time to delve in deep and search out information. Depending on where you live and your company policies, you may have a wide range of options for time off work (paid and not), coverage on medical expenses, and options for networking resources. This is only the tip of the iceberg.

You will want to visit the Human Resources department where you work to get the low-down on exactly what you are entitled to and when. You will treat everything as if it is predictable, even if it isn't.

Unexpected situations can still occur, and having the knowledge about your options can give you the tools you need to make quick decisions about what to do should anything arise. If you look into it later, there may be other consequences, and for some benefits, it may just be too late.

While we have already touched on the topic of financial planning, the hectic atmosphere of the first trimester is not the best time to load up on that worrisome mountain beyond realizing the basic structure of [Baby] = [Costs Money]. Hopefully, that was enough to make you start planning ahead by regularly putting some money aside. This game has no "get out of baby costs FREE" card. Unless you happen to come from very privileged circumstances, this responsibility is one that you will have to bear. As the looming reality of medical costs creeps closer and the reality of 'baby on the horizon' has set in, you can more rationally deal with creating a solid plan. You will need to make an honest assessment of the money that is realistically available to you against what you will inevitably have to spend.

Resources to explore in-depth include the following. Do not be optimistic with any of these amounts, as that will only tend to lead to a shortfall.

Your current savings. This should include what you currently have saved as well as what you hope to accrue. By 'hope,' that is what you have already assessed to be an amount you can comfortably put away with every paycheck.

Employee benefits. Time allowed off may seem like a good thing, but it makes a huge difference if that time off is paid or not. Paternity leave will likely vary from maternity leave, so make sure you read the correct section in the Employee Handbook. If you have that benefit, it can help you make a substantial contribution to the transition from pregnancy to experiencing more of the child's earliest moments on the planet and support your partner in acclimating to taking care of the new addition to your family. Read the Employee Handbook and be sure to consult with Human Resources to confirm you got it right.

Insurance coverage. While the company you work for maybe provide insurance coverage, you want to treat what they accomplish separately. This will have to do specifically with medical expenses, which will be the most significant portion of the baby bill. Like employee benefits, insurance will vary depending on your plan and the company that the plan is managed through. Read your policy and be sure to give Customer Service at the insurance company a call to be sure you reached the correct conclusions and that you are not missing any benefits or inconspicuous requirements.

Social support. Under this category, you are looking at the potential for pledges by friends and family. Assigning an actual figure to this sort of support will be difficult. The friend who professes: "Don't worry about it, I'll be there if you need me" may have no real intention of following through or may not be able to when the time comes. You might want to keep track of that in a 'speculative' column of your formal financial assessment. The real value of social support is more likely to be donations. Unused baby carriages, cribs, changing tables, and other accessories can save you a lot of money. Especially if money is going to be tight when you reach the bottom line, there is no need to be overly proud about something that will only get short-term use.

Government programs. Depending on where you live, your income, financial situation, and other factors, your access to government programs and social support will vary. This is another situation where research, networking, and consultation can pay off. You will want to look up government information as well as consult with your obstetrician.

Credit lines. While getting into debt may not be your first choice, it may be one of the only ones if your current resources are not sufficient. Applying for a loan or taking out a second mortgage are ways to finance having a baby over time. If you are a first-time father and have not done much to build your credit score, having a child and taking out a loan might actually help your financial viability — so long as you can pay it back. You will have to keep up on payments, but the fiscal risk of a responsible parent is something that financial institutions look on as a positive. It could help position you for investing in the purchase of a home or upgrading if you already have one that will soon prove to be too small.

What is a less interesting option is financing the baby with credit cards. This kind of high-interest debt is something you want to keep to an absolute minimum (e.g., the occasional purchase of maternity clothing) to keep the accruing debt off the baby-costs ledger. Credit card rates can be as much as ten times the rate for a home-owners or personal loan. This kind of debt needs to be a temporary fix if you want to stay financially flexible.

What your budget should look like. Some people will never have had to budget, and that is probably because it ranks on the fun meter something like scrubbing your driveway with a toothbrush. Even thinking about a budget sent my wife into diatribes of denial, exclamations of the task's impossibility, and all manner of avoidance behaviors. The goal of a budget is more rudimentary than all-encompassing. Write down what you know, and not mystery expenditures. As with all seemingly impossible tasks, break it down into steps by working away at the easy things first.

If you and your partner have been together for any time at all, you will have an idea of the costs you have from month-to-month or week-to-week for rent/mortgage, grocery bills, car payments, insurance payments, electricity/utilities, internet, phone, current credit debts, etcetera. Just list out the known costs and add them up and compare that to your income. It may be painful to look at, but waiting will only make that pain more severe. The bottom line will probably affect your decision-making and will force you to be responsible. If there is an apparent shortfall, the goal has to become how to make the ledger balance.

If you can't just sit down and get it done, you may want to engage the services of a financial planner. The bad thing about that is that it will cost money. The good thing about that is that a good financial planner will be sure you have a solid plan, offer proper financial advice, and you won't have the opportunity to blame your partner for making big errors in the estimates.

Future Planning. Along with the pain of financial reality come other practical aspects of living as a family. Life insurance policies should be reviewed or considered. Plans for improving quality of life over the long-haul help you put together realistic plans for moving into a suitable residence, planning for your child to attend good schools, and even helping to launch them into their independence as a young adult. Starting a college fund is not out of the question. Beginning a savings account for your child to deposit any cash gifts can eventually turn into an account the child can manage for themselves to help make them responsible adults. It can be fun to envision what the future may hold for your child, and starting them early can help set them off on a path that espouses freedom and success.

The Mid-Pregnancy Scan

Sometimes known by the unfortunate name of "Anomaly Scan," mid-pregnancy is another milestone that you should prepare for but not fear. At this stage of the pregnancy, the fetus is large enough that the sonographer can detect fetal progress, including normal, healthy brain development, bones, limbs, features, and other organs. Scans also look at the development of the placenta and general health of the mother, and conditions that may affect the pregnancy having nothing to do with the child. It may be cause for further testing, bed rest, or other precautions.

While there is the possibility that you will get news that reveals something, this only happens 6% of the time globally. That 6% also does not mean whatever was revealed is automatically cause for concern. The percentage will vary depending on the country you live in and possibly even where you choose to vacation. For those without known risk factors in genetics, environment, or habits, the percentage is reduced by about 50%. It is good to go in with a positive attitude expecting a glowing report instead of working yourself into a hand-wringing frenzy. Becoming anxious releases hormones into the system and can create an imbalance of the body; what may begin as needless fretting could potentially trigger unwanted issues.

Scans are not perfect and will be dependent on the sonographer's experience and expertise to some extent. The scan will also not uncover every possible defect or condition, some of which will never be apparent until after birth, and some not until years later (e.g., colorblindness). It is also good to remember that everything considered a 'defect' is not necessarily serious, debilitating, or cause for concern. I was born with a preauricular pit which sounds ominous. It is just a tiny hole in front of the ear. My first daughter was born with the same condition, and when I saw it, I was actually a bit flattered that we shared an obvious common trait. But the key here is that fretting does nothing to change the outcome. The other side of the coin is that the scan will usually result in confirming that everything is progressing well. It is also possible to discover the sex of the baby. Know beforehand if you want that to be part of the discovery.

The scan itself is not invasive and will usually take around thirty minutes. There may be slight complications in getting a good view due to the positioning of the fetus and possibly the mother's own anatomy, but just hang in there, be patient and supportive of your partner, and reign in anxiety. If it wasn't obvious: be with your partner for the scan! It is incredible that some people choose not to attend this chapter in the miracle of birth and prefer not to be there to support their partner. The scan is not mandatory, it is not harmful to the mother or child, and the peace of mind it can offer is well worth going through. The results are available immediately, and some sonographers may give you a running account based on their style.

If anything is found during the scan, you will be informed, and any options you have will be explained. If a second technician either attends the scan or does a second review, it may just be the hospital's policy. The technician may have limited experience or may request a second opinion to ensure that all the results are correct.

Immersing Yourself in Understanding Trimester #2

Just like in the first trimester, there are certain things you can expect to be part of the baby's development, changes in your partner, how you fit into your role as an important part of the script, and maybe even what you've learned about yourself so far. We'll have a look specifically at what is going on, just like we did for the first trimester because when you know, you are a better partner.

* What is happening with the baby?
* What's happening with your partner?
* How can you best be of help?

What Is Happening with the Baby?

The baby has become recognizably human by the 14th week and is only going to start growing more rapidly. Starting at about 4 inches by week 15, the fetus will grow to about half an inch per week, getting up to about 9 inches by the end of the trimester with growth in bodily length accelerating.

During the first month of the trimester, the fetus begins to sexually mature, with males forming a prostate and females developing ovaries and what will mature into their life-long store of eggs of their own. Hair will grow along with a mucus-like substance (vernix caseosa) which helps to protect the skin in the aqueous environment where they are developing.

In the later months, the formation of hair extends to eyebrows, and other fine physical attributes such as taste buds mature. Your budding flower is essentially a miniature human in every way by the end of the trimester and only goes on to advance in these stages of development in the approaching trimester.

The "lump of clay" had made a significant advancement in taking final form. Remain diligent and alert to dangers in the environment. Try and be helpful with your partner's diet, which will continue to morph and flourish. Everything that passes her lips still plays a part in the development of the child.

What Is Happening to Your Partner?

Around week 13, many women begin to both experience the rambunctious effects of hormones as more tolerable and grow more accustomed to simply being pregnant. This trimester is the easiest part of the pregnancy for most women, and it will hopefully come as a welcome respite for you. There are, however, no guarantees. But you may see a smile more often, and the fierce swings in mood may become less volatile. At the very least, things should not get worse.

Don't let that suggestion make you think changes in her are finished. She may begin to experience other pregnancy symptoms, like joint aches and unusual flexibility. Her body is going to start seriously adjusting to what it needs to be able to do at birth and bust that bowling ball through the eye of that needle. Relaxing plays a major role at this point which helps relax smooth muscle tissue and foster growth of the placenta. While flexibility may initially seem like a benefit, too much of a good thing can lead to loose joints, injuries, and problems performing seemingly simple tasks like walking or standing up. It is nothing to be tremendously alarmed about but something to be aware of. If mom has difficulty, she may need to take it easy to avoid a serious fall and may need your help — at times more than she would like to admit. Remain understanding and resist the urge to dote.

Another biologically stimulating change your partner will experience is the enhanced presence of estrogen and progesterone. This will stimulate melanocytes' production, which affects the balance of melanin in her skin and can lead to a range of conditions. If she usually has clear skin and begins to get a bit blotchy, chances are she will not take to that kindly. She may develop a lina negra, or darkened line, vertically at her belly button. Her nipples will probably ripen to a darker shade, and moles or freckles may be affected by changes in color and possibly size or shape. It is important to note these things so they are not mistaken for something more serious. Cortisol and Human Placental Lactogen levels will fluctuate, affecting blood sugar levels, blood pressure, and metabolism. Unless anything seems to go haywire and she is experiencing persistent secondary symptoms, these changes should all be temporary and will not be dangerous to the mother or fetus. Simple changes in diet and exercise can control many resulting issues. She should consult her physician with any concerns.

Those are the common menu items. She may have any of these along with side-orders of indigestion, shortness of breath, congestion, constipation, gingivitis (or similar symptoms), fatigue, flatulence, swollen feet, blurred eyesight, and circulatory discomfort that may result in spider veins. Last but not at all least, there will begin to be physical evidence of what is growing inside. That baby bump and its swelling may be just what is creating some of the issues. As it expands in the limited space allowed, it starts to push organs out of the way and physically stress systems by putting pressure on them. In all, the smorgasbord of symptoms, annoyances, and issues will probably pale in comparison and nearly seem to be a relief when compared to troubling nausea and relative insanity of the first trimester. It may well be that simple systematic desensitization to the initial onslaught has made her a better warrior, stoic to the mere, trifling challenges that emerged. She has made it this far and, as such, has fought an admirable and inescapable battle. Let her know that you admire her effort.

How Can You Best Be of Help?

You, Prince Charming, will want to do all you can not lose the beautiful qualities you have nurtured in becoming a better human during the first trimester. You want to continue to nurture her, understand, help guide her to sound decisions for the sake of all, and hold fast to the righteous path. But now you have practise, you've grown as a person, and you are already a model that other newly expectant fathers can emulate.

Aren't you?

Here is an excellent time to take inventory of what you learned and did well, but hardly time to start awarding yourself prizes for excellence. People have to practice for a long time before they truly become good at something. Be aware of what you accomplished, know what worked and didn't, and learn from your mistakes.

Just like you needed to concentrate on maintaining friendships as a takeaway in the first trimester, don't let yourself get caught up in inactivity. At the outset of being a dad, your partner is going to have plenty of reasons to rest. She has to protect the asset she is carrying. She will be drained by doing nothing more than her body taking over to stoke her incubator. You might want to eat in sympathy so she won't feel bad for gulping down extra portions, but you don't have the same engine burning your fuel. You might try to involve your partner in walking or other exercises that benefit you both, but if you allow yourself to bloat out, you aren't going to get rid of a whole bunch of it in a birthing ordeal.

Stay mindful as to how to keep fit. Don't go punching elevator buttons when you can take the stairs. Don't try to find the closest parking space unless you are delivering precious cargo. If you are, act as a chauffeur and drop her at the door, then valet-park your family craft like it was a new sportscar that you don't want to be dinged on the first weekend you bought it. That means long and far away from the door so that you have to walk it. She'll still be checking in at the waiting room desk when you get there, and you'll have put in some extra steps. Put an app on your phone and try and set a goal for steps every day. Take a walk at lunch. Fill that step count, and if you see your own baby bump start to grow, up to your daily goal.

Contrary to most people's beliefs, walking can be just as beneficial as running. It is less stress on the body, easy to recover from, and has good cardio. Before this is all over, you are going to have still another leg of that marathon to run, and you will want to take it in stride while remaining healthy and prepared to take on fatherhood for the long haul. You are not too busy to get a little extra work in. You can clean while she rests, take the dog for a walk — anything that keeps your engine burning like your partners will be without her slightest effort.

Women will adjust to the changes in their bodies in different ways. Some may feel down about their metamorphosis. Here is where your reaction can make all the difference. If you communicate in a loving way that you sincerely enjoy the changes and stress the importance of her efforts and your joy in the idea of your growing family, that should come out well. Assuage her doubts about her appearance, be communicative, stress the positive, and you might find a benefit in growing your intimacy as a couple. Her response may take you by surprise, especially if the romantic side of your relationship took a vacation during the first trimester. You have to understand that it just isn't fun to make whoopie when you need to be sure the vomit bowl stays within reach.

You did great to get through that first trimester, and you will do fine in the second so long as you embraced your role, worked at being a great partner, and rewarded yourself for noticing the positive part of what you have done for yourself and your family. Don't lose sight of your friends and support network, keep making time for physical and mental well-being, and take joy in enhancing your relationship and interdependence. You are about to enter the third act of the play feeling like you've got the hang of this partnership thing. It may be a quiet celebration, but there is nothing better than taking on the challenge and improving yourself.

Parenting and Partnering Power

Homework for the dads to be right now includes taking inventory. If you made an effort with your notebook, birthing plan, and finances, you are going to be in good shape from the planning perspective. Continue your personal growth with diet, exercise, and stress training.

Professionals who use planners never write things down one time and never look at them again. Update your plans from time to time to incorporate what you learned or remembered you forgot. This means looking at your birthing plan and notebook to update everything that needs it. Change all plans that have evolved as they are bound to over time and as you gain experience.

It isn't a bad idea to do a monthly review because a lot of times, you will find yourself saying, "yeah, I wanted to add that." You might even pick a day of the month to do your reviews. It won't take you hours to do. Just a couple of minutes a month for review can keep you miles ahead in making your plans detailed and successful.

Writing helps you think and discover, and you may come across better scenarios as you revise.

Chapter Four:

The 3rd Trimester - Months 7 to 9
(Weeks 28 to 40) of Pregnancy

In some ways, the third trimester is the most intense, primarily because of the extreme changes in the fetus, the mother, and the eventual onset of the actual birth. Things have become very real in an obvious way that they have not made themselves known before. The parents and everyone close to them are seeing the short ramp to the birth and beginning to anticipate the actual arrival.

However, although the finish line may appear to be insight, this is no time to let down your guard or start cheering a victory. All you have to do is look up "Premature Celebration" on YouTube. You can find all manner of examples of the tables turning when athletes give up their effort mentally before they actually achieve their end. While pregnancy isn't about winning, it is definitely about finishing the marathon, and finishing well counts whether you lead the pack or crawl in with your knees scraped as your best effort.

Your newly established fatherly habits are going to continue to carry the ball. They save mom some trouble and are something you will want to maintain. While you can look forward to a balance beginning to return sometime after the baby is born, don't count on going back to your pre-pregnancy lifestyle even then. You have taken the red pill.[1] By engaging in accepting this partnership in parenthood with your partner. There is nothing particularly scary about taking the pill, but there is no un-taking it now.

Just as before, your knowledge will prove to be influential in fielding the third trimester. If you are not surprised, you are way more prepared to handle your responsibilities well. Your reality is looking forward to the brand new experience of fatherhood and life as a dad. It will be even more of an adventure, more enduring, and likely more enjoyable than the pregnancy itself.

Time for a Review and Zapping Procrastination

If you have screwed up to this point and not paid attention to the suggestions and details for planning, you will be penalized by having to reread the whole book. Do not pass Go, do not collect an award for the best partner. Just as a 'for example,' planning would have been best to start at the turn of the first few pages. Have you started it yet? Let's see a show of hands.

Like anyone with a master's degree in procrastination, you probably have not been awarded with a trophy for being last in the class. In procrastination, he who achieves most procrastinates least. Achieving high scores in procrastination is one time where you do want to fail. You may have had one friend in high school who didn't leave every paper until the night before it was due, but my guess is that with class in session, just about every reader is going to tie at this finish line and admit they are still putting off things they should have accomplished months ago.

Because I am aware of the propensity to procrastinate, a quick summary of what you have already learned is in order so that you start taking things a little more seriously. This review should revive your memory of what we have already covered in previous trimesters, but the review will not be repetition. Some are reviewed,

---

[1] For those who are unfamiliar, this is a reference to the movie "The Matrix." Two pills are offered to the main character (played by Keanu Reeves), allowing him to remain in blissful ignorance or face a life-changing truth. By taking the red pill, you have done the latter.

but this section adds specific differences for the third trimester for each point to build on your previous goals. No playing hopscotch and jumping to the next section; these are the core values to becoming a third-trimester super dad.

Continue to Be a Partner to Your Partner

You guys have probably learned a lot about each other and learned a lot about being better partners. This part of your experience should continue to grow. Take what you have learned and expand on your skills of:

* Communications
* Recognizing her physical burden
* Staying on protection alert
* Sex and romance
* Achieving a different kind of easy

Communications. Talking about the future and continuing to nurture plans can put her mind at ease. It will make her feel that she is not alone in the practical concerns of being a new parent. Showing interest in how she feels and using your evolved communication skills will end up working out for you in the long haul. Continue to respect her motherly instincts, and don't be afraid to ask her for guidance as to what else you can do. You've got plenty of fun things to chat about. Why not start with circumcision? You'll have more of an investment in that than the color of the walls in the baby room. (See Chapter 1)

Recognize her physical burden. Nothing is getting much easier for her at this point. She is pretty much strapped to a medicine ball, and it will tax her physical skills and endurance. Eating may look like the only thing she is good at doing at times, but eating takes energy and persistence, especially when the kid you are giving a free ride to is doing their best to squish every organ you have into the size of a walnut. She might want to eat that whole pizza. She may need to eat that entire pizza. But her stomach won't accept it. Help her help herself by rising to that challenge not to feel compelled. Always be alert to ways you can genuinely help. She might get stuck on the couch and will want to get up instead of having you bring her something. Help pull her up. (See Chapters 1 and 2)

Staying on protection alert. All encounters with obvious threats to the mom and fetus should be avoided. Even if the danger of the most severe issues is lower, they have not disappeared. If you have done your job admirably, she will be feeling a little spoiled and maybe even feel entitled to certain indulgences. Still, no chewing on lead-coated pencils, engaging in toxic fine art recreation or testing out questionable herbal teas that might provide laxative effect to relieve the resident-imposed squashing of her digestive tract. As warned in a later segment of this chapter in more detail, do not let her resort to chemical removal of unusual hair growth. That is worth mentioning twice. When in doubt, consult a doctor. (See Chapter 2)

Sex and Romance. If there are no complications, sex is still a viable option and one you will want to be honest with your partner about exploring. This is no time to wrangle her into selfish advances. She may be tickled to know that her appearance has not changed the way you feel about her in any negative way. But if she is resistant, kind words and kind gestures may go as far as a lusty romp. (See Chapter 1)

Achieving a different kind of easy. You've both endured six months of the pregnancy, becoming closer through the challenges and planning for the future. In a way, the third trimester is a little like after you've done six months at a new job. It isn't new anymore. You probably both see the humor in some of the things you've learned that is now old hat. You've made it this far together, and the hindsight of rifts you might have had in more ridiculous moments are things you can laugh about. You've gone to war and come home safely. That is how bonds grow.

Review All Plans

If you have begun to plan, you haven't finished, and if you have missed planning opportunities, time to catch up. Review all your plans and amend them to incorporate what you have learned.

* Budgeting
* Have the birthing plan at the ready
* Have the hospital bag at the ready

Budgeting. This is the one thing you were warned not to neglect. If you really have not looked at it and made a plan, it is imperative that the two of you sit down and go about completing the task. It is probably one of the most unpleasant things you will have to do, and it will be even more unpleasant and confusing now that you have waited this long. Do it and keep yourself from digging a financial hole, or worse. You need to cover time off, mom's needs, baby's needs, and medical costs. If you've got a plan in place, you are a champion and just need to review it and consider revisions. If not, sit down and budget now. (See Chapters 1 and 3)

Have the birthing plan at the ready. There should be a written plan that is really a ledger of doctor names, numbers, and essential information that needs to be prepared on the day of the birth so that it can be accessed easily. This can contain all the weird little details you and your partner want, like the kind of music that should be played (trust me, you won't notice who is serenading the birth). Who else is attending the actual birth can be important. The birthing room itself is not a stadium. If your mom or your partner's mom wants to be there and they are not the type you want in a war room, politely decline. This, really, optimally, is an intimate gathering of essential individuals. Your partner has to be there. If your partner wants you there, you should be. We had a nurse who was a friend of the family in attendance, and that was a great relief because she could explain all the stuff I didn't understand.

Catch the baby, or not? That's one you want to think about, dad. I absolutely refused. If anybody was dropping anything, it wasn't going to be me, regardless of my fielding percentage in baseball. I'd never heard the end of it. On a scale of 1-10, how much do you want to avoid an episiotomy? On a scale of 1-10, where do you weigh in on epidural? Some of these things will fade from your control because that's why doctors are in the room. But you want to get your preferences down. If you started the plan months ago, bravo, my brave knight! Now update it with everything you thought of afterwards.

The unwritten plan should also be ready. That is mostly a daddy-do where you take a hospital tour, know the route and alternates, and plan for unforeseen circumstances. One of your most important jobs is to keep gas in the car all the time. I used to have a habit of flirting with how close the needle could get to the letter 'E' on the gas gauge without running out. During the period of the final trimesters, I was keeping my car full, and when I got home, I'd check my partner's car just in case. (See Chapter 1)

Have the hospital bag at the ready. On the day of the awaited event, you don't want to be fishing for your toothbrush or anything else that you'll need during your hospital stay. If you have not put the bag together, do it now and tick it off the list. You cannot count on precisely nine months or 40 weeks being right to the day. This bag is at the ready by week 30, or you are neglecting your responsibilities. (See Chapter 1)

Don't Neglect Yourself.

You may not be the primary player, but if one of the members of the team goes down, it isn't going to be you. You need to be there to help hold her up and keep her pushing toward your next adventure of parenthood. The only way you will do that is by being of sound mind and body. To that end, you need to:

* Stay fit, alert, and maintain friendships
* Watch the weight gain
* Breathe and meditate

Stay fit, alert, and maintain friendships. The most significant change you would want to make from the original outline of taking time for yourself is taking time for both of you. She may feel less motivated to maintain any exercise regimen simply because it is harder and more uncomfortable to move. Choose light exercises like walking or ask to participate in things you notice she might not be doing anymore. Saying something like: "Can you teach me some yoga that you've been practicing?" puts her in the position of being the expert, and she may like that. Encouragement is the key. The last thing you want is for her to lack the stamina she needs for childbirth because you dropped the ball in motivating her. You also don't want to get a call from the hospital while you are out at a pub with friends that the baby came early. 'Congratulations,' you missed the entire experience you've been waiting nine months for. It won't be worth it. (See Chapter 1 and 2)

Watch the weight gain. There is a suggested range of weight that women should stay within during pregnancy. There is also a warning for men. While women gain weight during pregnancy, men usually do, too. The odd trade-off is that a bunch of the weight she is gaining is somebody else's, and yours is all you. According to various sources, men gain an average of 15 pounds from being exposed to new snack opportunities, eating out more, and eating for two, even when there is only one. Along with staying fit, stay aware of extra calories you are allowing yourself that you shouldn't, and maybe make it up in some other way. You can pack smaller lunches for work and knock off fewer Friday beers. (See Chapter 2)

Breathe and meditate. This is another potential group activity that will accomplish a different goal in the final trimester. If you have successfully incorporated breathing exercises and meditation into your routine, helping your partner practice can provide another weapon against the trials, persistence, and rigors of childbirth. It is a stressful time and getting mom to be able to create self-imposed calm may quell what can be self-defeating anxiety. There's no way to guarantee stress-reducing regimens will have the baby drop out with greater ease, but as long as the practice is not extreme, it may help you contribute in a meaningful way to the experience in the birthing room. (See Chapter 2)

Further Your Education

Of course, you haven't learned everything yet. That will come your second time around when you can look at the first one and say: "He told me in the book, and I just didn't pay attention." Next, we are taking a brief look at some topics and specific concerns that may not yet be in the scope of your radar.

* Utilize your experience resources
* Pertussis vaccine
* Kick-starting labor

Utilize your experience resources. I didn't exactly say this in the introduction, but having no experience with a baby will mean you have none. Changing a real baby is nothing like changing a dummy. Holding an actual child will test those skills and give you valuable experience you can build on. If you have friends and relatives with kids and infants, being around them can help your education. The difference between before — when you wondered why people had to ruin a perfectly good BBQ with a bunch of brats — and now, is that you will soon be the one ruining the BBQ. That's not the entirety of it. Now you have a vested interest in paying attention to how others parent so you can learn from them. Up to this point, other people's kids were like so many flies landing on the burgers or wasps hovering around the grill. Now they are your little teachers. Watch what makes them not cry. Select from the menu of things you will and won't do with your own kid. Hold babies. Friends and family will be amused and glad to offer advice. Don't drop the baby.

Pertussis vaccine. In some countries, the Pertussis vaccine is recommended for all pregnant women sometime between the 16th and 32nd weeks of pregnancy. Getting vaccinated during this period allows for the antibodies to be passed from the mother to the fetus with reliable transmission time. These vaccines provide protection against whooping cough, polio, tetanus, and diphtheria (there are some variants to the Boostrix IPV vaccine, so it is best to ask your doctor specifically which variant he will be using). Whooping cough is the primary reason for the vaccine. Babies who get whooping cough often require hospitalization, and the vaccine effectively prevents whooping cough in 91% of cases studied since 2012. Studies have shown little to no side effects besides very minor redness, swelling or tenderness for mom as might happen with any injection. The vaccine is optional, and with the swirl of misinformation about vaccination due to COVID social media doctors and misinformed anti-vaxers, there is probably more resistance to vaccinations now than ever. This is despite the overwhelming good vaccines have done for the health and welfare of humanity. Unless either the mother or the father has had some type of severe allergic reaction to a vaccine, there is virtually no reason to have any concerns about taking it. Much better to do this than to risk a potentially fatal hospitalization stay for pneumonia.

Kick-starting labor. There is a lot of information on Google about things that will help start labor. Some are simple and seem not to be dangerous, and others are reckless and ridiculous. The things to try if you need to are harmless ones which include having sex, exercising, nipple stimulation, acupressure, and eating certain foods (pineapple, dates, eggplant, spicy food, etc.). If what you are eating is not weird and in amounts that can be toxic to mom or fetus, it may at least satisfy you that you are trying to get the ball rolling. It would be hard to say that you are doing anything by the time it gets to this point. Whatever seems successful may just be a coincidence as you won't be working at starting the engine before the due date anyway. In our first run, my wife and I were sitting on the couch watching something like "America's Funniest Home Videos," and someone got their tongue stuck on an ice-cube tray. We both started laughing, and then she blurted, "get me a towel!!" There was nothing in me asking why by this point. I ran to the closet and brought back assorted colors. Then we grabbed the hospital bags, hopped in the car, and we were off to the hospital. I sort of like that it happened with a laugh.

The idea of inducing labor is something else entirely. When you get to around week 42, and the contractions still have not begun to convert to labor, the doctor will let you know it is time to induce. It is probably best that you leave decisions of this magnitude up to the experts in the long run. However, it is also good to keep in mind that there is a bit of a downside to inducing labor. Recovery tends to be slower. It is impossible to say if that is directly related to the induction or just because the pregnancy is on overtime. The other thing is that contractions can be more intense, as can be the pain of labor. This may be a reason to add a clause to your birthing plan along the line of "If induced, then epidural."

Immersing Yourself in Understanding Trimester #3

While many things may seem to have become routine over time, it is evident that other things keep changing virtually by the day. The one thing that may not be subject to change is you; the hope is you have successfully formed yourself into a rock of consistency, improved as a human, and you are tipping the scales measuring the applause for your performance. You still need to keep your radar on what's going on.

* What is happening with the baby?
* What's happening with your partner?
* How can you best be of help?

What is going on with the baby? Until this trimester, the baby has been doing more to grow in length than in girth. The baby will bulk up almost 50% over the trimester, and that comes in the way of organ development and shaping into what you recognize as a newborn. The eyes will open somewhere around week 28, and the fine hairs that have been protecting the skin for the past months will begin to shed. Right about week 35, the baby will shift its squished position so that its head will point down in order to exit head-first. It doesn't always happen, and that is considered a 'breach baby,' affecting about 5% of births. It can lead to complications, but it is really not a major concern in a situation with well-trained staff (doctors tend to be well-trained).

One of the most important things that will be going on throughout the trimester is the development of the lungs. One of the reasons premature babies have a rough time is that breathing is an issue because the lungs do not have the chance to form fully. Development goes on throughout the trimester; that is why it is best to go full-term. Even if mom is a little tired of being a free ride, she should not be doing anything to promote early labor unless at the suggestion of her physician.

The baby sleeps about 90% of the time and can REM sleep and dream. While sleeping most of the time, that does not mean there will be a lot of inactivity. Just like watching your dog chasing imaginary rabbits through the underbrush, the baby may exhibit activity even while sleeping. The baby will be practicing many things that will come in handy when finally escaping their holiday chamber. They may be smiling, frowning, and crying, and essentially taking baby steps in their development.

What is happening with your partner? Until this point, there hasn't been a tremendous amount of stuff you've needed to know about your partner that you can participate in beyond lending a helping hand and exhibiting patience. Things change here as much more becomes obvious, and your partner's personality starts to play into her role as bun bearer. She may be frustrated with all the things which make her experience technical difficulties as if the little darling on the inside is pulling marionette strings on the outside.

It is tough to say just how the 'little lady' is feeling at this point about going from however little she was to however big she has gotten. The average weight gain during pregnancy is about 30 pounds, including the baby (and other things that rapidly exit during the birth). This weight gain can present in various ways, such as enlarged breasts, fat reserves, and blood and fluid volumes. The frame of the mother before the pregnancy will matter when it comes to total distortion, as will any special diets. My mother was a small woman who miraculously gained only 15 pounds during pregnancy, and I was almost 10 of those. When the birth was over, besides reminding me forever that I almost killed her for the next 45 years, she was looking about the same as before she got pregnant the day after I was born. That is not normal, and the excuse was that she was on a special, precautionary diet which somehow had absolutely no effect on my growth but was critical for survival.

You don't want to try and have your partner mimic that performance because it is unlikely. However, you do want to pay attention to the expected range for gain. Your doctor will likely tell you what that range should be and will issue a warning if mom goes off the rails. In general, petite women should gain much more, both by percentage and in total, than women who are already a bit on the plump side.

These changes may be distressing to moms who are not used to seeing themselves with extra weight. My spouse was tiny all her life. Born at 2.7 kilos (just under 6 pounds) at full term, she held to just 43 kilos (95 pounds) without change over the ages of 18 to 31. As her athletic body started to morph because of the pregnancy, she knew she needed just to accept it. A week before birth, she weighed in at a 'monstrous' (for her) 61 kilos (about 135 pounds). In other words, she came up to the top end of the average for her height for women who were not pregnant. There was 50% more of her to love. Somehow her metabolism managed to knock almost all of what survived the birth back off her frame in record time. Her experience was nearly the polar opposite of my mother, although the baby size was similar. In all, the safe thing to say is that the experience will be different for every woman.

What the fantastic final third of incubation does manage to do is distress the pregnant partner in one way or another — and likely several ways at the same time. Pre-pregnancy framing and metabolism play a part in where everything gets squished too. Especially at the end of the trimester, it is safe to say that any woman's framework will be like a balloon inflated to just that point where no more air can go in. Then the baby is going to try as it might to just get those few more tiny puffs in, or else it isn't really testing the quality of its ride. Your job is primarily to stay aware that mom will be uncomfortable.

Wacky stuff goes on, and some of it is really interesting. Other parts leading up to the ultimate event may just seem a little gross depending on your level of tolerance. Some can even be a little frightening. You can think it, but don't say it. Try not to make faces either. You want to keep your meter dead center between "Oh, it's nothing" and "I'm calling 911" at all times. Accept that things will present and you haven't seen them before. It's sort of like having the doorbell ring and knowing when you open it up, you are either going to see an alien or not. Best to try and look at it all with wonder rather than trepidation and assume all aliens come in peace.

Several things present in ways that will be pretty apparent. While her normal head of hair may seem even more lush and beautiful, she may start to grow hair in places that she might not particularly care for — like her face, nipples, and back. This is most likely an annoyance that will reverse after the birth. Do not let her use chemical treatments of any sort to defeat this strike to her vanity. If it absolutely drives her bonkers and there is a need to attend to her vanity, offer to help her out, but always be kind and supportive if you do. Depending on your relationship, she might prefer that a friend's hand be put to the task of depilation.

Some cute can happen in the manifestation of body-in-change besides just the omnipresent belly bubble. Her belly button may pop if she does not already sport an outtie. Her areola may darken and change shape and size, which is thought to be so that baby will have an easier time locating and latching on. Breasts can also vary in various ways, usually to enlarge and become more firm. Regretfully they may be sore sometimes, which may have started even before the diagnosis of pregnancy way back in week 1 or 2. By the third trimester, the aches and pains of becoming engorged may make the largeness of her breasts seem even more enticing than usual. Careful there, bucko! You may like what you see, but it may not be the best time to display your affection. Remain conscious that they may be particularly tender. On the other hand, you only really have to avoid sex if 1) she is not interested, 2) everything is not progressing normally. If her water breaks or there is another discharge, use good sense and hold off for a more reasonable time.

During this trimester it may seem that every part of her has been injected with a little gremlin and wants to have the opportunity to complain. For example, even the most athletic of the female species is likely to experience some form of shortness of breath. This may be more noticeable to those who have particularly good habits of breathing from the diaphragm. As there is no longer much space for the diaphragm to move downward, breathing may be more shallow. Of course, this is complicated by the fact that she is breathing for two. Reminders to maintain good posture over slouching can actually relieve some of these symptoms while regretfully calling for additional resources that she may feel she has run out of.

The squish-squashing and extra weight assembled in such a short term may mean a change in an exercise regimen. Very low impact aerobic efforts like walking and exercise classes, especially for pregnant women, may be just the thing. Don't wait for her to figure out what she needs, and be on the lookout for opportunities such as public pool memberships where you can accompany her to work out with recommended regimens together. Don't, don't, don't go at it like a viper because she might think you are insulting her new curves and are overly concerned with the way she looks. Always keep the context of partnership and baby welfare. If going the public pool route, check reviews to ensure the facility has an impeccable reputation for cleanliness and safety. Besides the obvious exercises for flexibility and fitness, she should probably be doing kegel (pelvic floor) workouts several times a day. You can help with reminders. These can help during birth and may yield other benefits in recovery and return to a somewhat enhanced sex life when all is done.

She may complain of vague numbness or pain in the lower back, butt, and shooting pains that radiate down her leg. This is her sciatic nerve complaining about the pressure on it because it too is being squeezed. Warm compresses, simple massage devices (or her partner's gentle hand), exercise, or even just changing positions can all contribute to relief. In moments where it becomes intense, some pain killers might be considered as a last resort. Be sure to check with the doctor before ingesting anything, especially if it is a miracle cure found on some suspicious website or in a well-meaning YouTube video.

Mom may experience premature contractions, known as Braxton Hicks contractions. It is probably best to just think of these as practice for the real thing. They can come on in various ways but will most likely be something like a cramp, a solid muscle contraction that mom is not doing intentionally. Of course, it is possible that labor can start prematurely, and it is best to be able to know the difference. Braxton Hicks contractions are irregular, and if there are clusters, they tend to get weaker. Often they can be relaxed just by changing position (standing up, walking, etc.). Real contractions will not just be clusters that dissipate. They will keep coming in waves and will tend to get stronger. While that is still a bit vague, contractions for actual labor will come every 5 minutes, lasting one minute, for at least one hour. This may be accompanied by a discharge (e.g., water breaking). In other words, you need to take contractions seriously when they seem insistent, or like the last guest at a party that gets on the phone and calls some people to come over to liven things up a bit when the party sputters out.

The baby is active and kicking. There will be significant downtime, but there will be moments where the baby will seem to be trying to break out of the shell-like it is in an egg with limbs flying nearly like a kickboxer. How easy these are actually to observe on a bare belly will come down to fat reserves that have been stored, but they will be apparent to the touch. The doctor may suggest monitoring baby movements just to track the frequency to ensure everything continues to progress nicely.

Mother's trips to the doctor will increase to about every two weeks and may be as frequent as once a week as the trimester comes to a close. Always attend when you can, and when you can't, be sure someone goes with her. Can she go by herself? Sure. She is probably doing a lot of things by herself. Living humans will be like that, and especially if she is feeling perky, there's no reason she can't be alone. But give me a good reason why.

One thing she may be spending some particular amount of time within a variety of different ways is deliberate forms of nesting. This can be in the form of cleaning and preparing, fussing with the arrangement of baby things, watching cooking shows, reading about taking care of newborns, watching programming that seems peculiar to her normal regimen, etc. This more likely has to do with embracing the mindset of being a mom and having had nine months to appreciate that she is already responsible for the life of an entirely new human. Soon it will be kicking and screaming and laughing and being adorable in what seems more like real-time. Common sense says: "You've got to be ready; it's showtime."

The Pet Aside

If you have pets, they likely will have become aware of the fact that something is going on. Either cats or dogs will probably sense changes that humans just do not have the ability to. They won't want to be left out of the family event, and really they shouldn't be. You want to do as little to surprise them with a new alien and change their lifestyle as little as possible. The final word here is to take care of the pet, acclimating it to the situation and being sure that it will embrace the intruder who will be nabbing significant companionship time.

Practice taking the dog for a walk with an empty stroller if possible, so they are prepared for the real thing. If you can't get the dog to be your partner in walks with the carriage, now is the time to find out. It is better to watch them knock the thing over when it is unoccupied than when the buggy contains a precious cargo, and you'll have to contend with a baby rolling out onto the concrete. It may give you an idea of whether you can take care of two walks at one time or if you are forced to take two walks. An alternative is to hire a dog walker.

After the actual birth, it may be advisable to bring home something with the baby's scent from the hospital to create that familiarity before introducing the baby to the house. Surprise is not always the best means of introduction. No matter how acutely aware the pet may be or how intelligent, everything you can do to ease the transition is just another measure of smart parenting.

Cats will probably have made themselves more critically aware of being attracted to the cozy warmth mom is exuding. Just a reminder to keep mom clear of kitty litter as toxoplasmosis is never a good thing during pregnancy.

More care may be needed with exotic pets than typical domestics. It is best to keep any type of rodent away from baby (and mom) as they may carry a virus called lymphocytic choriomeningitis which can cause serious complications. Lizards, snakes, turtles, and other amphibians may carry salmonella and listeria monocytogenes. While you may have a deep emotional attachment to pets, you do not want to risk introducing the baby to a bacterium and have to rationalize the relative importance. In some instances, it may be best to face the facts and get that exotic critter out of the house entirely.

How can you help? You got this far, and you know it isn't over. Getting this far taught you a lot of things, and you are ready to push through. You have got to be the one who picks up the pieces that fall on the ground because a few months enter here that she won't see her own toes when standing in the shower. You have to review what you learned, review the plans, check, double-check, and step in to be the cavalry on call.

When you learn martial arts, the idea is not violence but a calm, natural reaction. When you go to break a board, you don't aim to do it by hitting the board because that's how you break your own bones. You want to strike an inch or more beyond the immediate target, so everything you have goes right through. You are not looking at the water breaking, the labor pains, the trip to the hospital, or even the baby's first gasping breath as the end. You have to stay on task past there and be a pillar of your new family. You'll remember your effort, and you'll do better next time if you have the chance. Your partner will have all the focus will get all the attention and credit, but she will also know that you did it together. Just like "behind every great man, there is a great woman," this is the opposite side of the coin.

Punch through that barrier.

Parenting and Partnering Power

You really have to corral the last-minute obligations going into the final stretch. You want nothing to be up in the air by the end of this trimester as you are getting down to game time. The home needs to be ready for the new arrival, and all your plans should be in place. If you have been working on them even a few minutes a week and doing monthly reviews, everything should be in pretty good order. Don't let that fool you. Keep up with what you know you have to do.

This trimester can be a time of bonding like you, and your partner will not have it again for a long time. You'll see the humor in things that were worrisome in the first two trimesters, the goal will feel like it is insight, and it will probably be easier to inject some well-intended humor into things that you may have been too nervous about joking about before. Keep to your regimens, and don't lie to your notebook. It knows. Stay rested, fit, and ready, and give yourself some credit for becoming a better partner.

Chapter Five:

The Fourth Trimester

While technically not part of pregnancy, the period following the birth is a time of significant adjustment. It is hard to put a period at the end of pregnancy and say it is all over as far as the dad's participation is concerned. In fact, it's not hard. It's wrong.

A book for dads about pregnancy would be remiss not to cover what happens in the few months following birth. It may not be fitting to extend too far into the future as that is the subject of a different book. Certainly, the period where your baby was not breathing the same air as you has passed, and the wriggling squirming bundle is out in the physical world. It is a new leg of the journey, but the following steps forward are like the close of a movie after the climax, which ends with a clever denouement, and you end up satisfied and looking forward to the sequel.

In case it hasn't sunk in, you are officially a dad now. The physical burden that mainly was the responsibility of your partner has arrived, now is the time you can do some actual sharing of the physical child. Your family now has three members, for better or worse, and you are headed on a new leg of the journey.

What Happened in the Delivery Room

Because you paid attention to all the planning and details laid out in this book, your hospital experience during the birth went swimmingly. The water broke, you hopped in the car, and you made it to the Emergency Room doors without running a single red light even though you had to track around a water-main burst. Your partner was admitted, and you parked the car in under a minute and were back by her side in three. The birthing plan was followed to a "T", and — boom — out came baby without any effort. If you are paying attention to the sarcasm, that is likely not what happened.

Labor may have lasted far longer than you expected. The average is about 8 hours. You only think it is a lot quicker because of what you see on TV or in movies. Do you know why labor goes quickly when produced as part of a film? That's called drama and allowed storytime. Movies can't take eight hours to show a woman going through all the pains of labor, and it would blow their budget and the box office if they did. The people who are really invested in the birthing room are the parents living the real drama and the good people seeing them successfully through the experience.

Our first-time labor was a total of 16 hours. Things on the birthing plan did not pan out exactly, and probably neither will yours. Your regular doctor may have had three patients go into labor simultaneously, so while they may have been in contact with whoever filled in for them, they may not have made the actual delivery, especially if they work in more than one hospital. Your partner may have kept her head through the stress and pain, or she may have turned into someone you had never met before whose hand you were trying to hold while she slapped it away with a poly-syllabic swear. You may both have become delirious from sleep deprivation, and the baby was just beginning to show the incredible ability to misunderstand the word "cooperation."

Hopefully, you were able to stand by your end of the bargain, fight through dizzy spells and unexpected moments. Hopefully, the birthing plan eased you and your partner's navigation through the hours of delivery. Even if the plan said you'd cut the cord and you opted out while slightly overwhelmed, that doesn't make the plan a failure — and neither are you. The plan made sure you thought things through and knew the way it was supposed to go. Like a wedding, something always pops up to defeat what should have been perfect planning. It could be rain, the flower truck crashing, or the best man's phone battery dying, but in the end, the show must go on. At the very least, you've got this maiden voyage off your list of to-dos, and you will become world-wise from the event. Should you have the opportunity to experience it again, you will be better prepared, but things will still head off in unexpected directions in encore presentations.

Inevitably, somewhat frightening, things may have happened. More likely than not, these would only be frightening because you were not in on the details. My first child put me through some bit of unexpected trauma by arriving in a bluish tint and not taking what I thought would be the quick gulp of isopropyl-scented hospital air. Minutes before the birth, the doctor told me that there were some complications with an entangled cord and that really it wasn't much to worry about. Well, I took the advice and didn't worry, but that didn't exactly tell me what to expect. An entangled umbilical cord occurs in nearly a quarter of all pregnancies, making it fairly common. Just how it is entangled and where can make the potential result more complicated. If the cord is wrapped loosely somewhere, there may be almost no presentation or issues. If it is tightly wrapped somewhere, the entanglement may choke off the flow of the baby's nourishment through the cord as well as affect the baby's circulation to the brain. Of course, doctors who have seen this hundreds or thousands of times are not about to panic.

I saw my blue baby put on a cart after the cord was cut, limp, and silent, and I knew better beforehand not to participate in 'catching the baby' or 'cutting the cord.' Someone else's kid, no problem, but not my own. I watched as a nurse kept looking up at the wall clock.

The nurse walked round and round the baby cleaning things up and rubbing her feet, and all I could think was, "It's dead." It wasn't nearly the expected outcome, and I couldn't even look at my partner. No one said another thing to me as they were all set to tasks of tending mom, baby, supplies, and machinery as if infant mortality was no concern at all. There is where my education about childbirth failed. What seemed to me to be an interminable time between the baby's arrival and the first breath was no more than three minutes in reality. Time has a different meaning in stressful situations, especially for those who are stressed. The cord had indeed been choking her, but some quick moves by the physician in charge eased the baby's arrival and sped her to the cart. While I stood a few feet away, ready to barge in and slap the baby myself as I'd seen done so often on TV, that the first yelp sung out spontaneously, and baby blue pinked up in short order. Moments later, we were informed it was a girl (Yes, we actually chose not to know if it were a boy or a girl), and I was invited to visit the cart when I would no longer be in the way of people doing their jobs. Not to blame the doctor doing the delivery, but if she had just said, "the baby may be a little off-color and may not breathe right away," I'd have avoided that brief meltdown. But it isn't every doctor's job to present a class. I should have read that. Aside from the nurse looking up at the clock, no one was doing anything that showed concern. There were no machines being wheeled in, no respirator, no whispering huddles. I'd come to the game under-prepared.

As it turns out, there is about a 10-minute window before the baby will potentially experience more severe issues and much longer before the issue of mortality arises. Her initial APGAR was four, which I actually did know was in the range of moderately abnormal, and my personal education had gotten me that far. I knew that four was not the kind of number you wanted to hear, and I didn't know which things she was earning points for. Had I not been so panicked, I would have realized that she was getting zero points for appearance, zero for activity, and zero for respiration, but that also meant her little heart must have been beating. She was earning points for something I couldn't see from where I was standing (see the APGAR Scores sidebar). The happy part of the story is that once she took that first breath, her score jumped to eight, and the immediate danger fluttered away on the same wings on which it came. A lesson to learn here is that probably everyone in the room knows more about what is going on than you do. It's no sin to ask a question. Keep them to a minimum, and don't be a pest. Never tell your doctors what to do unless they ask your opinion.

APGAR Scores

APGAR stands for Appearance, Pulse, Grimace, Activity, and Respiration. The scores are a means of quickly evaluating a baby's relative health. The evaluations can be done several times, from immediately after birth through an extended period if there seems to be some concern. The rating is based on five categories where the baby can score from 0 to 2 for each category, with the highest score being a ten. The categories and points include:

* Appearance (0 — The baby is blue, 1 — the baby has blue hands or feet, 2 — the baby is pink)
* Pulse (0 — Below 60 beats per minute, 1 — 60 to 100 beats per minute, 2 — greater than 100 beats per minute)
* Grimace (0 — No response to stimulation, 1 — slight reaction to stimulation 2 — a clear reaction to stimulation)
* Respiration (0 — Not breathing, 1 — weak cry, 2 — strong cry)
* Muscle tone (0 — Limp, 1 — reserved motion, 2 — active motion)

The most confusing of these is 'Grimace.' All it means is that the baby reactsto a reflexive stimulus like a gentle pinch or another discomfort. This is hardly high science and does not require medical tools.

The test is given routinely immediately after the birth and then again five minutes after. If the five-minute test still shows an APGAR of less than seven, the score may continue to be monitored for an extended time.

We had three surprises during the birth, a late epidural (my partner wanted to avoid pain relief entirely because of potential risks), an episiotomy (once almost considered standard procedure and now used far less often, it was not on the birthing plan), and the wayward cord. My wife took the epidural as a last-minute call when she was offered the final opportunity (some doctors will do epidurals right up to the moment of crowning). The good part about waiting was there was less chance of affecting the baby because the time between the epidural being introduced and the actual birth was fairly short. The risk to mother and child is relatively low, but complications can arise.

You may have had a moment or two when you faltered as I did, but imagine how much worse that could have been if you had not been as well prepared. If you went a little woozy at the sight of some things that went on, hopefully, you hid it from your partner as her lady parts went through calisthenics that you never dreamed were possible. Your birthing plan should have included just how close you get to the action. If you know you get wobbly knees at the sight of blood, it might be best to stand north of the center of activity as you try to comfort your partner, or just stand back or even out of the room if it is not the place for you.

Other Birthing Options

It is probably true to say no one plans on a cesarian. That will probably be your doctor's call in response to some complication that is not easily resolved in another way. Obviously, this is a surgical procedure and will require a more hands-on deck. The prep and procedure will probably not take more than 30 minutes, but it complicates recovery time.

Mom will have to be placed on fluids and pain killers, which would not usually be necessary after natural childbirth. While it may not be the preferred option, just be glad it is available and accept that it was the best advice given to you. Be aware that c-section rates vary from hospital to hospital and doctor to doctor. You may want to enquire long in advance about the record of your ob-gyn and hospital.

Induced labor will be much like natural birth except with the preamble. There is no real surprise of the water breaking and unexpected contractions unless, by coincidence, normal labor starts on the induction day. It should end up being more like attending a doctor's appointment without any mad dash to the ER. This is usually an option used when the due date is overdue. Several ways of speeding things along include an Oxytocin drip, cervical ripening with prostaglandin (which relaxes the cervix through a vaginal application), and stripping membranes. One or more methods might be used depending on the difficulty of starting the engine or the reason for the induction. For the most part, induction will be the same as natural childbirth except that it is generally accepted to be faster and more intense (I.e., painful).

In all, your job as a partner remains about the same while the medical professionals go about their work. Good for you if you performed your role well. If there were chinks in the armor, learn from your mistakes.

Immersing Yourself in Understanding a Successful Birth

* What is happening with the baby?
* What's happening with your partner?
* How can you best be of help?

What is happening with the baby? Baby just got plopped out of its comfortable, warm nest into the bright lights and big city of a hospital room. It is a lot to get used to when compared to the muffled, dull plodding of the womb. No wonder most of them start crying almost immediately. The baby is tended to with any special care concerns, but mostly the focus will be on acclimating the child to mom and the new real world. The baby will be weighed and measured, given antibiotic eye drops, and a shot of vitamin K. The latter helps normalize blood clotting. They will take the baby's footprints for records and additional ID.

Before even leaving the birthing room, mom, dad, and baby will all get ID bracelets that they need to have at all times to be sure the parents are reunited with the correct children. The goal is to make the nightmare of a potential mixup something that is nearly impossible. There were tragic records in the past of babies being swapped at birth, but gladly the practice has evolved. In extreme cases, DNA could be used to identify the proper parents of a child.

Post-birth tests include hearing tests, blood tests, and observation for congenital heart defects. If required, the baby may be tested for HIV and hepatitis. If it is a boy and the option for circumcision is selected, it may be performed within the first two days. A practice becoming more common is having parents return after a week or two for the procedure.

Once you are out of the hospital, the baby no longer has the automated support system and protection of the mother's body. The hospital staff will not trail you home, and the baby is totally dependent on its parents for survival. Intending to that level of care, neither parent is likely to get a lot of sleep, and that will remain the case for some time until things settle into a routine.

What's happening with your partner? Your partner just went through a sudden colossal change in her physique. She might be the type just to shrug it off, or she may find the shift somewhat disorienting. She may be superhuman if she isn't at least a little light-headed, extremely relieved, or even giddy immediately after the birth.

Mom and baby will remain in recovery for two to four days, depending on whether it was natural childbirth or not. This may vary due to hospital policies. Regardless, mom's body will have to begin a process of repair. She needs to eat healthily, stay hydrated, and care for her state until her strength returns.

Rely on her to choose whether or not to accept visitors. People may have stayed in the waiting room hoping to hear the good news, but that does not mean they should automatically be admitted after birth to be the first to see the baby. Your partner will likely be exhausted, not feeling that she looks her best (despite and because of the sudden loss of 15 pounds), or may just need some downtime to get it in her head that the process is complete. She will probably be happy to have fewer doctors poking and prodding as if she were a science experiment and learning how to be a new mom is the premiere item on her list.

Breastfeeding is new to her, and the first attempts may be as soon as an hour after birth. There can be issues here as likely as not with the baby learning mom's anatomy and mom having zero experience. Hospitals will likely have a specialist on staff to consult for breastfeeding issues. It is important for mother and child to have that time to bond.

There are likely to be mood swings brought on by exhaustion, hormones, and simple emotional reactions to reality. Joy, disbelief, even missing having her baby inside her can come on her in a moment. The fluctuations may wear off in just a few weeks or may linger. In extreme cases, it may evolve into post-partum depression. Suspicion of the latter should be evaluated. In all, the hope is that things gradually return to normal for her and you over the next six weeks or so. Be her careful watchman, and don't assume it is time to leave your post.

How you can help. Your role as a father has completely changed when the baby emerges from the womb. You are not a player on the sidelines just tending to your partner (and yourself), but there is a list of new tasks and skills to develop. These will be things you already know we're on the way. Still, your previous experience with all of them has more likely been in the form of a fire drill than a fire (unless you did as suggested and explored your personal resources to get experience with actual babies).

The hands-on skills that you need to acquire include the following, and almost exactly in this order:

* Holding the baby
* Getting the baby in a car seat
* Diaper changing
* Feeding the baby
* Burping the baby
* Putting the baby to bed

Holding the Baby. Your baby is nothing like sporting equipment. The package is quite delicate and more like a priceless urn than a football. Newborns don't have much stamina, muscle, or coordination, and especially during the first two months, you want to pay particular care to support the neck and head. Keep in mind that said 'particular care.' The whole package requires your attention. You don't want to approach the situation with fear, but you really need to exhibit mindful gentility.

Until your baby shows significant ability to support the weight of their own head, it is literally in your hands to do it for them. When lifting the baby, always support the neck and head with one hand and the baby's bottom with the other. It may take a little practice to transfer to the cradle hold, but even for many dads, this will come naturally. As the baby gets older (over three months and supports the weight of their own head comfortably), you can experiment with other holds that will be more comfortable for you and the child.

Holding the baby will be something you will experience before you leave the hospital, whether someone hands you the child or if you go to pick it up on your own. Always err on the side of caution the first few times you hold your newborn, and don't be shy about asking questions or advice, and listen when it is offered. No one wants to tell a new dad it looks like it is his first time to the skating rink. Comments are made to help you and secure the welfare of your child.

Getting the Baby in a Car Seat. The next thing I am sure I did was awkwardly get my child into a car seat. I'd yet to leave the hospital parking lot, and after successfully managing to not dump her out of the carrier, I then managed to successfully maneuver her into place with the seat facing the rear of the car. I would swear this was only possible because I'd already put the seat in and taken it out a dozen times in practice. Do not make the mistake of thinking you'll just figure out the seat on the day you bring the baby home. While people picture the ride from the hospital to their residence as some type of fairy tale, if it happens to be pouring rain or the hottest day of the summer, you won't want to spend a lot of time reading instructions you forgot to bring. If it is that steamy hot day, be sure to cool down the car before getting the baby down. She might like to be swaddling warm, but she won't much like roasting in an oven.

Our hospital had a policy that a specialist would come out to watch me install the seat and be sure I got it right. It may be possible to request this service if it is not offered as standard practice. There's another gem to get on the Unwritten Plan. You do not want a simple pump on the brakes to spill your special cargo just because you didn't put in the time to get it right.

Diaper Changing. While you may have the opportunity to change your baby for the first time at the hospital, your first time may likely be at the homestead with the luxury of a dedicated changing table.

If that is the case, someone smarter than you has probably stocked the area with all the practical things you will need at one point or another to address the mess. It is inevitable that you will forget something and that your first few changes should be monitored. After just a couple, you will develop all the skills you need to improvise quick-thinking solutions to what-the-heck moments. Supplies may run out, and the baby will not have the courtesy to wait to do anything while in the midst of a change. Think of supplies like toilet paper and always replace the roll when it runs out.

In those more special moments where you learn that a diaper can weigh as much as the baby (or so it seems), you will keep your cool and manage to deal with the most prominent mountains of poop while leaving the area spotless and the baby free of diaper rash. Learn what you really need and wrap your head around the moments you have to pack the travel bag yourself. That time will come.

Feeding the Baby. Of course, if mom is breastfeeding, your participation in baby nourishment will be limited as far as the role you can play. However, when and if mom plans to go back to work, you pull split shifts or merely want to do your part to let your partner sleep, you have to be capable and knowledgeable about feeding the baby. Formula or milk that has been pumped and stored in the fridge should be brought up to the proper temperature. It isn't actually necessary to heat formula, but if you consider the original source, the freshest supply of milk with being about 98.6 degrees. The word 'about' is in there to acknowledge the fact that breasts may not be precisely average temperature because not all people are. They are also often wrapped in extra garments and extend from the torso, so it is hard to say one way or another that there is a perfect temperature. It does, however, seem counter-intuitive to provide the baby with something they might find less comforting and satisfying by sticking them with a cold liquid diet.

Be careful not to overheat the milk. It is not a bad idea to use a double boiler. You can even just heat a bottle in a pot of warm water. Just run warm water off the tap and place the bottle in. No matter how you do it, always check the final temperature of the milk. Some mysterious force might be at work to thwart your best efforts. Make sure the milk is mixed well by tipping the bottle a few times end-over-end and putting a squirt on your wrist. That isn't an exact science either, so err on the safe side.

When using powdered formula and mixing your own, you want to ensure that the water source is pure and does not contain high amounts of chemicals commonly found in tap water like fluoride and chlorine. In cases where you are using well water, it is probably best to boil the water first for several minutes and allow it to cool. In most cases, tap water should be safe, but it may be advisable to take extra care depending on where you live. If using bottled water, check the ratings on purity. It won't be within everyone's budget to install a purification system, but even those will vary in effectiveness and viability.

Ensure that all formula or breast milk is stored correctly, and take care to observe limitations as to how long you leave it out. It is far from impossible that you can create unsafe conditions for milk storage, especially when you are out and about with a travel bag. Be careful about promptly emptying bottles that have been used and keep things clean if not absolutely sterile. No one likes this sentence, but: read the manufacturer's instructions for handling all bottle-feeding equipment!

Burping the Baby. One thing that dads can probably relate to is a baby's need to burp. If the gas stays down when you eat too fast or knock back a carbonated beverage, it just means you'll be uncomfortable. Well, that goes for baby too. Air that slips by the suckling is going to be uncomfortable, and until it bursts free from entrapment, it is cause for discomfort at nap time and crying jags.

What you are trying to do in burping is create an environment where tiny bubbles in the tiny belly merge so they can escape in one whopping yodel. The favored methods are tapping the baby's back just below the shoulder blades or rubbing. The result is the same thing: introducing gentle vibrations encourages the bubbles to merge. Please note the word 'gentle' as key to success and avoiding anything more abrupt that might be considered shaking the baby.

The easiest way for most new dads to do this is to throw a burp nap (also more notoriously known as a vomit rag) over your shoulder and then cradle the baby's bottom in the right arm to face toward your chest and toward the rag. Spend some time tapping and rubbing the baby's back. The bubbles will collect and escape.

The level of violence of the escape is sometimes why you need the vomit rag. If you often get a milk shower and your partner does not, it may be that your feeding technique is encouraging the ingestion of air. It may be worthwhile to revisit your style and pay close attention to the differences between how you and your partner feed the baby. The little effort might save a few t-shirt changes.

Putting the Baby to Bed. Times where you may assume the greatest role as a hero is when you can manage to get the newborn asleep when your partner has been at it for hours. It is sometimes an achievement to develop confidence in getting them back to sleep in the middle of the night. Things that might keep a baby awake that are obvious to moms — and dads tend to forget — are a change of diapers or a bit of a nip at the baby bottle. Of course, gas of more than one sort may be keeping the baby awake with stomach or abdominal discomfort. A gentle massage may be just the thing.

Tricks do work sometimes, such as bringing the baby out for a ride in the stroller or the car. Cutting across a playing field once, I found that taking our stroller with super-sized wheels out over a lot of open grass created a motion that was lulling. The ride was a bit less smooth than the asphalt, and it seemed to be a trick that worked often. Be sure to keep car rides to those times you are alert enough to drive.

Another popular method to work with is sound. The womb environment is dark, and most of the fetus's sensory stimulation is auditory. Considering the baby is permanently submerged for those nine months, sounds tend to be muffled and rhythmic, like breathing or the pulsing of blood. So while people sometimes turn to what they recognize as music as something that will be lulling and comforting to a baby, it may not be the best choice. Lullabies were created for a reason, but sure, babies may prefer jazz, classical, new age, or even rock. When you find something that works, try and expand on that library. Don't be surprised if the sounds that lull your baby will not be those you find lulling yourself. It sounds like summer storms may have a similar effect on infants as they do on adults, and simple white noise like turning on the shower can be simple magic.

Pay attention to the position(s) your child prefers to fall asleep in, and if you never have, try different positions. Upright, cradled, and face down can all produce different results, as can rhythmic rocking or moving about with a bit of a bounce in your step.

Take care when placing the baby in the crib. The baby should always be placed on its back, especially in the early months when it cannot navigate on its own. Keep the immediate area free of plush toys, pillows, blankets, and other things that may look attractive to an adult but may not be best for the child's safety during sleep.

Parenting and Partnering Power

You have graduated from pregnancy school, and now you are a dad. The list of new skills you have to learn here is less mysterious when the pregnancy is over and the baby is here, mainly because you can see what you are working with. Pregnancy was fraught with emotions and the unknown processes you could not see, and in fatherhood, things are primarily hands-on and happen in the real world. That will be to your advantage. Take advice and learn from experience, and everything will be just fine.

Don't just chuck that daddy notebook. If luck should have it that you will be a parent to a newborn, later on, this will be a great record book of what happened. It will also be a way to learn about the mistakes you made because your personal record is going to be the most valuable thing you have going forward. Even if you have a good memory, that notebook will make it better.

Conclusion

A Sentimental Journey

You've seen the pregnancy through to completion successfully, and you have mostly managed not to botch anything. If you have given it your all, you have improved the state of your relationship, even if it was good before. You've enhanced what and how you share, which bodes well for the future.

The journey of pregnancy was one you took together and has unfolded in the blossoming of new life. If you have taken the advice in these pages seriously and followed up on suggestions, you had an easier time tackling this first experience with pregnancy than most men will, and you enhance the health and prospects of your relationship and family. This was not just a journey of sweat and tears; it was a learning experience that has made you a better partner and a better dad. Just like training for a job, the skills you learn will seep over into other parts of your life and help you embrace responsibilities you would never have trained for otherwise.

After the child is born, one distinct difference you may begin to notice between yourself and your partner is that she will tend to want these years to last forever. While you will have fun and enjoy the experience (most of the time), you might not be able to hold down your enthusiasm for getting your infant to do guy things with you, like playball. I admit that I wanted to start my first in games of skill a little too early. On the other hand, I did end up enjoying those years in a dad sort of way. I suggest that you don't rush these years of infancy. Just like you couldn't push the accelerator on the nine months of pregnancy, all will come in time. Prepare yourself to consider what else you can gain from this part of the experience. Some people call it mindlessness, living in the moment rather than constantly pushing toward the future or, worse, trying to change the past. If you waste the opportunity you have now, it won't come back. At some point, you may end up looking back with an empty portfolio of the early years of your child's life and wonder where they went.

It may be that you don't really have fun cooing and when a group of women get together to talk about babies, the whole sense of joy washes over you like words of gossip over a fence. You'll volunteer to fill snack bowls and top off drinks just to get out of the room. What you really want to do is look for those moments that end up being distinctly "dad." If cooing is not your thing, leave the cooing to mom and focus on the things in your child's world of wonder that you can enjoy. It isn't a good idea to go against your partner's wishes, but there are times I let my kids do things that might have made their mom frown. Nothing dumb like playing in kitty litter but exploring the world with not so nimble little fingers. When it came time to crawl around in the grass, being part of that experience by pointing out the dandelions and things that might ignite discovery created a different kind of joy. Showing a baby how to dunk an acorn into a plastic bucket is a skill level some will manage before their first words. But that is a connection and the beginning of communications with your kid. Things that became commonplace long ago to you are all new to your child's eyes, and maybe they are a way for you to see the world anew again. The smallest things might bring them the greatest satisfaction, and this tiny thing you brought into the world can, in turn, be that source of satisfaction and discovery for you.

I read to the children from a very young age, and all remain avid readers. My second child loved reading so much that she had a physical response to the words she read. It was like she was getting plugged in. One child walked so early she became a danger to herself, and I felt I had to follow her around like a human rubber baby bumper. Many times she'd end up heels overhead anyway. Another never crawled at all, instead of using her own creative means of locomotion (I've heard it called scooching and scooting). People would stare at her as she zipped down hallways in hotels cause she could really move. Each of them was like exploring a book uniquely about their discovery of the world and themselves. As they got older, I knew them better because I watched them develop, and their behavior arose as hints to what would make them uniquely themselves. I learned from them, and I hope they learned from me.

Soon enough, your kid will get to the age where you feel more in your element. You may even end up missing some of the more mundane things that came to pass as they grow because you can't be there all the time. But this whole process of mastering pregnancy and fatherhood is something no one is born with. It is a hard-fought battle of perseverance and will; still, the payoff is enormous. Learn to enjoy the moments, and they will stay with you forever.

Parenting and Partnering Power

You now have the tools to help you understand what is to come. My hope is you can now look forward to exploring the world that is opening up before you. Be a participant who is willing to learn and continue to grow by staying the course. This part of the journey means learning new things whilst relishing the memories. Dwell on the good ones. They say having a memory is virtually the same as living through the event. Pick and choose the good ones, and you are just adding scoops of the good ice cream on top of the cone.

I would be glad to hear your feedback about this book, both from the perspective of how it applied to your experience and what you learned from your real-life experience that could have been included here. Feel free to email me at: http://williamhardingauthor.com/.

If you think the book was helpful and that it is worthy of a nice review, please leave one on Amazon or your venue of choice. This will help dads that you don't even know to prepare for this phase of their life and look forward to enjoying their future.

Thanks for reading this work. I look forward to creating more in the future.

You may not be ready to do it again just yet, and your partner may not be either, but like everything that slides into the rear-view mirror of life, you can always look back with a greater appreciation.

REVIEWS

As an independent author with a small marketing budget, reviews are my livelihood on this platform. If you enjoyed this book, I'd really appreciate it if you left your honest feedback. I love hearing from my readers, and I personally read every single review.

JOIN THE DADS CLUB COMMUINTY

DAD's Club: Support Group For Dads | Facebook

REFERENCES

A CONTEMPORARY GUIDE FOR DADS,
STRATEGIES FOR THE 1ST YEAR
THAT EVERY FIRST-TIME FATHER NEEDS

NEW DAD
BABY HACKS

WILLIAM HARDING

NEW DAD BABY HACKS

A Contemporary Guide for Dads
Strategies for the 1st Year That
every First time Father Needs

By William Harding

Introduction

"Any man can be a father, but it takes someone special to be a dad." – Anne Geddes.

A nurse in scrubs just handed you a bundle, and holding it feels foreign. It is a bit of a wriggly thing and seems uncomfortable, like a butterfly emerging from a cocoon. It seems like a doll that little children play with for a moment, but this one has life-like skin. It looks a little other-worldly and a bit alien. You are unsure if you are looking at reality or a vision brought about by sleeplessness. The nurse congratulates you on being a new father from the other end of your tunnel vision.

You suddenly feel like you are juggling eggs and nearly drop the bundle. Your head pops as if waking up when nodding off at the wheel of a car. This is a newborn, and the little bundle is yours. It is what you spent the last nine months changing your life for so that you could safely get here, to this moment, holding the brand new life you created with your partner. As if on cue, it starts to cry. Or it may have been crying the whole time, and you are just beginning to hear it. You know you are already doing something wrong and your experience as a father has barely even started.

This baby is pretty complicated. It has moving parts you can't control and is powered by some artificial intelligence. There aren't any buttons or knobs to make it easy to operate. It isn't like the camera you just bought to document your experience of fatherhood.

Immediately, you want to look for the owner's manual. You think to ask the nurse a question, but she seems busy with other important things right now. Besides that, you have no idea what to ask.

You feel about as comfortable as if someone handed you a live salmon. A crying salmon. What would you do with a salmon? Hand it to your partner. She'll know what to do. She always knows what to do with things like this.

-----

*As helpless as that sounds, that's what it could be like if you go into fatherhood blindly. Every cry and whimper will just be telling you that you've made yet another mistake. Within no time, you'll want to do everything you can to keep from touching the baby, so you don't set off its alarms. All it will ever tell you is that you are doing something wrong, and you want to avoid the consequence of the rejection. It will stay that way until you learn what is really happening.

* Here's the truth. What seems to be the interminable announcement of your failure is just a baby crying because that is part of the way they communicate before they learn to talk. Any avoidance you practice will make the baby sense you don't want to be there. You have to get in and take your lumps and snubs for a little bit until you get used to the baby and it gets used to you. The crying will just keep happening, but at least you can tell that your effort and wait were successful.

*The hard truth is that children do not come with a manual, but they do have built-in mechanisms designed to make you pay attention. What they are saying as they cry and wriggle is a natural and innate way of communicating what are, for now, their basic needs and discomforts. These pages are here to help you make sense of the new language and prepare you for all the nuances of taking the helm as a dad.

This book is your owner's manual for the first year of your baby's life. It provides a holistic view, not just the simple nuts and bolts of the baby but also what will likely happen to you, your partner, your relationship, your environment and the world around you. You'll discover a plethora of tips just as you'd expect from any owner's manual, such as:

- How to baby-proof your home
- The real reasons why your baby cries
- Working with the baby's feeding schedule
- Problems that keep your baby awake
- Soothing and bonding with your infant
- What to feed your baby and what to avoid
- Keeping the relationship with your partner strong
- Exercising your baby's mental and emotional health

No matter how you have prepared for this part of your life, you will be surprised and likely amazed at the experience itself because it is anything but predictable. A whirling dervish entered onto your stage and will deliver a performance — part angel, part chaos. Even with the best preparation, you are guaranteed to experience something distinctly new and perhaps be surprised by fresh emotions. The sooner you come to terms with the chaos and rush of new emotions, the sooner you experience the joy of your little angel. Or something like that.

This first year will help you set the tone for a life-long relationship with this unique, new, unpredictable being. You can't expect to mold or itemize what is to come with any certainty, which is part of the delight. The one guarantee is that this will be an experience like no other. You hold the ticket for the trip of a lifetime, and it is time to find out what to expect along the way.

One thing you can never really know before it happens is how you will be as a father. Everyone handles the stresses, joys and changes differently. Knowing what's to come gives you a leg up on the situation. The thing you need to do first is survive the 24 hours after the baby is born.

Chapter 1

Surviving the First 24 Hours After Birth

The first few hours after your child's birth will be pretty intense, no matter how well it goes and how prepared you think you are. The first 24 hours are not so much critical but more a matter of adapting to the nuance and reality of being a dad.

Right at the moment of birth, you should have already made decisions about "catching the baby" (where you actually step in to have a literal hand in the delivery) and cutting the umbilical cord. You really can't have a weak stomach to do this or be prone to fainting. The doctor will assist you to be sure you don't do anything wrong. But you can not wait until the last minute to decide. Remember, you can always change your mind about stepping away from hands-on involvement if you start feeling wobbly in the knees. I do not get queasy and never passed out, but I was afraid of making a mistake.

You will mostly notice a bit of a mess in the first few moments after the birth. The baby will come out squashed, mottled and coated with vernix — a substance that has helped shield the baby's skin in utero. The goop and goo might be a little overwhelming if you don't know what is coming. I distinctly remember the afterbirth plopping out as if my partner couldn't stop herself from ejecting her organs with the child, as if the dam had broken. Even when you know that is coming, that's a moment even your partner will never see and to be honest, I am not sure I am happy I did.

It is worth noting that some cultures promote eating the (placenta). It is a rather unique, temporary organ — just there to serve its purpose during pregnancy. It is also something that has cultural meaning for some groups. It is used in traditional Chinese medicine and is commonly ingested by many species of animals. While I am an adventurous eater, this was beyond my personal scope of culinary interest, and no doctor ever suggested it. The act has gotten press in recent years as a celebrity fad and may be more popular with alternative birthing styles (e.g., people who choose to do water-birthing or those who use midwives). There are claims that the organ contains a mixture of nutrients and hormones that can help the mother recover from birth more quickly. But as many resources say, any benefits are offset by toxins that the organ stores and can pose food safety concerns. Some believe that any benefits are psychosomatic. Medical advice is outside this book's scope; therefore, it is up to you to do the research to see if the option interests you.

Your baby may be a little blue initially, and the wailing cries you expect may not be immediate. When the baby starts to breathe their first breaths, the color will shift to an expected shade. Remain calm, trust in the expertise of the people there to do the job, and breathe deeply. During the birth of our firstborn, the umbilical cord had wrapped around the baby's neck and she came out blue and not breathing. As the nurse carried the baby to the incubator cart, it seemed limp and lifeless to me and a deep panic set in because all I saw was a stillbirth. That was one thing none of the prep classes and materials I came across ever mentioned as a possibility. The nurse maintained calm as she went about her business, wiping things down to clean up, rubbing the baby's feet, and repeatedly glancing at the clock. I could not even look at my wife because I wasn't about to let on about my panic.

I felt the urge to jump in and whack the baby's behind like you may have seen on TV, in movies or in videos. My cooler head prevailed as I knew I had to trust the experts; there was no way I knew more than them. The first cry burst out a moment later, the child became animated, and her color changed almost immediately. Little did I know that motion would begin a cascade that would be difficult to quell. Until school began, that girl wouldn't stop moving all day until after she was asleep. One thing to take from my experience is to realize that the doctors know more than you do. They will generally let you know if there is cause for concern, like they let me know about the twisted umbilical cord.

A few tests take place almost immediately. The nurse will measure and weigh the child as they go about their routine. They take an APGAR score within the first minute of the birth to measure the relative health status of the baby. They continue to take APGAR measurements if the score remains below seven. See the "APGAR Scores" sidebar for more information about the test.

APGAR Scores

APGAR stands for Appearance, Pulse, Grimace, Activity, and Respiration. The scores are a means of quickly evaluating a baby's relative health. The rating is based on five categories where the baby can score from 0 to 2 for each category, with the highest score being a cumulative score of ten. The categories and points include:

* Appearance (0 — The baby is blue, 1 — the baby has blue hands or feet, 2 — the baby is a normal color)

* Pulse (0 — Below 60 beats per minute, 1 — 60 to 100 beats per minute, 2 — greater than 100 beats per minute)

* Grimace (0 — No response to stimulation, 1 — slight reaction to stimulation 2 — a clear reaction to stimulation)

* Respiration (0 — Not breathing, 1 — weak cry, 2 — strong cry)

* Muscle tone (0 — Limp, 1 — reserved motion, 2 — active motion)

The most confusing of these categories is 'Grimace.' All it means is that the baby is showing a reaction to a reflexive stimulus like a gentle pinch or another discomfort. This is hardly high science and does not require medical tools.

Your doctor or nurse will likely offer a vitamin K shot for the baby, another thing you should decide long before it happens. Vitamin K is important for blood clotting and the baby's levels of this vitamin will typically be low, especially immediately after birth. The shot is known to decrease the possibility of haemorrhagic disease (a serious and potentially fatal bleeding condition). There are negligible risks associated with the shot and no known allergies. The worst thing that can happen is bruising at the injection site (usually the leg). Drops are available, but they have proven to be less effective than the shot and must be administered several times to be effective at all.

As things calm down, the reality of having created a new life will begin to sink in. You may want to make a few phone calls just to announce the newborn news to family or close friends. But it is probably more important for you to remain in the moment and share the experience with your partner and the child in your first moments as a family. This is not a performance that gets repeated and if you blink, you might miss it.

Not long after things become tranquil and the doctors and nurses file away, you will have the opportunity to witness the possibly awkward and beautiful first attempts at your partner breastfeeding your child. While it seems like it should be the most simple and natural thing on the planet because it has been going on since the beginning of the human race, breastfeeding may not be simple or automatic. The child's motor skills are brand new to them, and your partner has never had the opportunity to practice as a nursemaid. The harmony and comfort in the experience is as clumsy as a boy asking a girl to the dance floor for that first dance.

If all goes well, the bedlam of cries and complaining will turn to the practical silence of suckling. But if it does not — and don't expect it to — the frustrations of your partner and the hunger pangs of your baby will steadily mount with time. That time is measured in minutes rather than hours and days. It may not come easily, and there may need to be more than one attempt at the initial feeding, but with patience, it will come.

Depending on the time spent in delivery, you may be exhausted and irritable, but this is a moment where your strength and stoicism needs to shine. Your partner will be far more battered by the struggles of the episode than you and you need to be supportive of her efforts just as you have been supporting her during the pregnancy. You've only got to hold it together for a little while longer as your break is coming soon.

Many hospitals will have support services to coach your partner in the initial attempts at breastfeeding. If a lactation consultant is available, there is no reason to wait to engage their services. It can be a comfort to your partner and the baby to have a consultation — even if everything seems to be going well — just to be sure the nursing experience is optimal. Specific details in positioning can make the difference between functional feeding and being proficient.

As the baby feeds, a coach may promote more skin-to-skin contact. This has various advantages, including calming the child, elevating the chances of successful feeding and helping to regulate body temperature. As that first feeding progresses, you can watch the baby melt into a sense of calm. The wriggling, complaining and clenched fists come gradually to rest as the tight little fingers begin to open and relax. After this feeding, it is usually time for a nap.

You may have felt some distance from the immediacy and reality of your new situation throughout the experience of the pregnancy, but now it will begin to sink in and feel very real. Your baby may be more familiar with you and your partner than you know as they can hear your muffled voices in the womb. They probably won't see you very well at all as controlling any and all parts of themselves is a bit of an evolution. Continue to talk to them and get up close when you have the opportunity. The more you reinforce your presence, the quicker they will come to accept it. In that area, mom clearly has the upper hand.

You Might Go Home Alone

Your partner and the baby will stay at the hospital for at least a day or two following the birth. The inpatient care time will vary depending on the circumstances. For example, if the delivery was by c-section or episiotomy[2])or there were other complications, the stay may be longer. Some hospitals are set up so fathers can also stay for the duration, but that will vary from hospital to hospital and it should be something you have on your discovery list when you take a tour of the hospital.

Whether you have to leave or stay, it may be a good time to review any photos you took if you had the presence of mind to take any during the event. It may not only help you wind down, but you can make sure that you have them arranged in a way that is viewer friendly — especially if there are photos that other people really don't need to see. You want to do something pretty simple as you relax, and reliving the adventure may give you an idea of the photos you missed and may still have the chance to take, like with doctors and nurses or maybe some early family shots.

Whatever you choose to do, don't do it while driving home. Concentrate on the road. You should not be tempted to text people about the news while driving. You will probably feel a little exhausted if you don't already, and your family needs you to get home safely. Turn on some music or listen to anything that might keep you awake.

If you have some swing time to be alone between trips back to the hospital, it might be a good idea to continue the quest you started during the pregnancy as a super-partner. Assuming you have been good to your partner throughout the pregnancy, you have already created some habits you want to maintain. Being there for your partner — especially in the weeks after the birth — is something you will need to concentrate on, especially if it was a difficult birth. When you are with your partner and the child, hop in to change

---

[2] an incision between the vagina and anus that expands the opening for the baby to pass through

diapers. Beyond setting up some very practical things like getting necessities, you probably haven't thought much about dividing up the new responsibilities that come with a baby. Responsibility sharing will depend a lot on work commitments and how much you accomplished during the pregnancy to look ahead. In any case, this is definitely the time to start thinking about what matters now that you have successfully navigated the pregnancy.

If you left your house in a rush after the waters broke, look around to see what you can do so that your partner comes home to a clean house. Do routine chores like washing dishes, mowing the lawn, vacuuming, or sweeping. Start looking around the house for things that need childproofing and make a list. You will have a while before that needs to be completely taken care of, but taking it a little at a time will help you keep sane. You can also do it in stages to cover crawling or scooting, standing, and walking. My eldest walked early, at about six months. I'm pretty sure it was more dangerous than the youngest who scooted for almost two years. Looking back it was highly reflective of their personalities.

Baby-proofing Your Home

A lot of things that once seemed harmless to you are going to turn out not to be. The most obvious things you will want to invest in are baby-proof electrical outlet covers (make sure they are not a potential choking hazard) and cabinet and drawer locks. You might want to look at a few options because some are more convenient for you and safer for the baby. Designs may be dictated by the handles on the cabinets and drawers. Corner guards for sharp furniture might save a whack on the head and inconsolable crying.

The other wise investments will be in baby gates for every room that will have to remain off-limits and any stairways — often top and bottom. This is another component of baby-proofing where the designs might make a lot of difference. For example, if either parent has mobility concerns, you may not want a gate you must step over. Gates you must remove often need to be put back quickly and firmly. Using the excuse, "it'll only be a second," is never reliable. Whatever you buy needs to be secure and safe for the whole family. Check with consumer reports and parenting sites.

Look around at your low shelves for any knickknacks, fancy plates, books, bottles, medicines, cleaners, chemicals and pet food that need to be moved to higher shelves. It may be silly, but crawling around your home might get you a few laughs, a little exercise, and a baby's-eye view of potential dangers. You'll spot electrical cords that dangle, waiting to be pulled. They all need to be shortened and tucked securely away. Watch out for where you charge portable devices.

Things you might not typically consider may also need to be dealt with. Unsecured furniture and shelving units might need a bracket to permanently secure them to the wall. Got a nice expensive large-screen TV? It needs to be braced if it isn't already.

Other than that, consider plants, your store of plastic shopping bags, any rocking or moving chairs, toy safety (e.g., materials used, potential choking hazards) and faucet covers (to prevent accidental baby burns). A must is investing in a baby monitor and keeping the crib clear of plush things (from pillows to stuffed animals and bumper pads). Many studies show they are not a good idea and could be a hazard.

Surviving the first 24 hours with your newborn will be filled with brand-new experiences. Drink them in and learn what you can about the person who has suddenly become a very real new member of your family. You and your partner will need to work together and be wholly responsible for many years. Right now, the child is the most vulnerable and least able to take care of themselves. The bigger problem is that you'll be responsible for providing the basic things your baby needs, and you may have absolutely no experience doing that. This is why the next chapter will dive deeper into that subject.

Dad Hacks From Chapter 1

Baby Prep Hack #1: **Think Like a Baby.** When it comes to baby proofing, you can't be too careful. While it may be a bit before your child can roam freely, you'll want to lock down every part of your home as soon as possible. Your bedroom, your bathroom, the kitchen, the living room; find every corner, chemical, and crevice that your baby could possibly get into.

Baby Prep Hack #2: **Your Newborn May Look Odd; That's Okay!** Babies can look very strange when they are first born, but there is no reason to worry. Your baby may have bent legs or feet, puffy/swollen eyes, and may even have a blue or purplish hue. Remember, your partner has just been through a very challenging event; freaking out about how the baby looks will not help. If you are concerned, talk to your doctor, but for the most part, your baby will look "normal" within 24 hours.

Baby Prep Hack #3: **Skin-to-Skin Contact is Important.** Skin-to-skin contact is essential between the mother and baby in the first hour after birth. If your partner is unable to facilitate this contact, you will have to do it yourself. Skin-to-skin contact after the birth is a huge boost to bonding. Hold your baby and make eye contact with them; this will help them feel safe and calm.

Baby Prep Hack #4: Make Sure Your Partner Gets Rest. Your partner will be physically and emotionally drained after birth, and they will need help getting proper rest in order to recover. Try to take the reins of baby care in the first 48 hours while your partner gets an opportunity to relax and get their strength back. Taking care of diapers, helping with feeding, and tending to your partners needs will go a long way to getting them back on their feet.

Baby Prep Hack #5: Discuss Breastfeeding. Breastfeeding can be difficult at first, and your partner will need reassurance if the baby is having trouble latching. You can consult specialists at the hospital, a lactation consultant, or your primary GP for advice on how to help your partner. They will be emotionally raw, so make sure to take responsibility for finding these specialists and fixing the problem A.S.A.P.

Chapter 2

Basic Care for Your Baby

"More often than not, the secret of success lies in the very basic, the very small wins. The small, consistent and disciplined steps lead to big successes."
— *Abhishek Ratna*

Now that you got your baby home, a bigger challenge begins. Learning to raise your baby will be a work in progress regardless of how much you have read and studied. There is no rush to become an expert at everything. There are some more significant mistakes you'll want to avoid, but you don't need to sweat the small stuff. Take small steps to learn a little at a time, and expect to goof some things up. Always keep in mind that you have a partner to lean on for help.

The first potential error you want to avoid is not treating the newborn gently enough. It is a little like a china doll. This is especially true for babies before they develop neck strength and other associated motor skills. You must support the head when holding the baby and in every position. If you don't, it can easily flop and cause injury. Be mindful that the head can flop in any direction, so you must protect it from all angles.

Cradling the baby in your arm is one good way to prevent any problems, but remain aware of head and neck at all times, including when feeding, burping, and changing. At times it may be more comfortable and practical to support with a firm hand on the back of the neck. That says 'firm' and not 'forceful.' Too much pressure might be as bad as too little. When putting the baby down to change its diaper, placing it into a carriage, car seat, or another carrier may be the least comfortable because you will be holding the baby away from you to place it down. This is where you will support it with your hand behind the neck just below the skull with your open palm. Squirming might make this a little tricky. Take your time. There is not a lot that is good about dropping the baby. There is absolutely no room for rough play.

Try not to forget about the importance of sanitation. The baby will have antibodies and an immune system, but it will not yet be well-developed. We are probably all more well-aware than we'd like to be of the importance of keeping your hands clean because of the experience with the pandemic. Maintaining a good regimen of washing your hands or using sanitizer before handling the baby makes a lot of sense. You may notice that doctors wash their hands a lot during your baby visits. That isn't just obsessive-compulsive disorder (OCD). It is good practice. You will also want to maintain a regimen for the baby when changing and after feeding.

Always make sure the baby is strapped into carriers and that you are using infant-appropriate devices. Anything that makes them sit up too straight in these early weeks will not be ideal. Read the instructions. There will be safety tips that are important to digest and best practices to follow. If you buy something used, request the user's manual or check to see if you can find one online. Carry out checks of the ground underfoot; for example, if you are holding a baby carrier seat and walk out on some black ice, that may be a disaster. You also want to be careful if you go out to the supermarket. Stacking a carrier on top of a shopping cart is not a good idea. On the other hand — and I am hoping it is unnecessary to say this — don't leave the baby in the car.

If you or your partner can't manage to go food shopping safely, make up a list with your partner and volunteer to get it done while she cares for the child. Don't forget to list brand names and sizes. If you have ever been sent out to buy feminine hygiene products, you may be familiar with the unfamiliar wall of choices. I had that experience and with no idea what to do. I just watched other shoppers for a few minutes picking things out, looked for places where the shelves were depleted and made the best guess. Of course, I came home with the wrong item and was sent back to the store. This can happen with anything. If you don't take notes and your list says 'cereal', coming home with Captain Crunch instead of Cheerios will find you slogging back to the market again.

Changing a Diaper

This is probably part of being a dad that it is difficult to look forward to. Once you get used to it and work out a regimen, it becomes second nature, and it really isn't as awful as you might think in concept.

Before bringing the baby home, you should have already decided whether to use cloth or disposables. Some people like the simplicity of disposables, but it may be interesting to look into diaper services which I found to be about the same price. It is far more environmentally friendly than plastic diapers that will last forever. My spouse and I used a combination of cloth for regular use and disposables in the diaper/travel bag. The reason is the cloth has to be emptied and sometimes rinsed before going into the wash hamper. Not very easy to do when you are out at a store.

Whatever your choice, you have to learn to work with it. Disposables were easy to put on and dispose of. The cloth frightened me initially because I feared jabbing the baby with the giant safety pins. Practice will get you everywhere.

Keep your supplies loaded wherever you plan to do most of your changing. It is not OK to leave the baby unattended on a changing table so you can hunt for supplies. You obviously need diapers and extra pins if you are using cloth. Keeping ointment and diaper wipes on hand is good because you will need both to wipe up. A towel or other cloth diaper should probably go under the baby to quickly work out 'accidents'. If you change a boy, you may be in for a fountain when you get the diaper off. It is wise to be ready in self-defense. A container to dispose of used diapers and wipes is also a good idea. Your diaper bag should be just as well-equipped.

To change the diaper — whether #1 or #2 — you want the baby on its back. As you peel off the diaper, don't be in a hurry, as you may not know precisely what you will uncover. You can use a washcloth or wipes to remove any residual mess. When changing a girl, wipe from front to back to avoid causing urinary tract infections (UTIs). Rashes can occur even if you are good at keeping up with diaper changes. I applied ointment every time to be proactive about rashes. That doesn't have to be a special product. For example, Vaseline works in a pinch. Diaper rash can become severe and get infected if left untreated. Wash your hands after changing, just like you would when visiting the bathroom.

If diaper rash happens, it may make the baby uncomfortable. It is just another reason for new opportunities to cry. Make an effort to be sure the child's little parts are clean after a change. Be gentle wiping the rash, be sure that ointment is applied and that you don't allow diaper changes to go over-long. You may change the baby about every hour of the day, including in the middle of the night. It may be good to check more frequently if a rash appears. A rash does not mean you've done anything wrong. The baby's skin is sensitive and some babies are more sensitive than others. If the rash does become infected (bleeding lesions), it is time for a trip to the doctor.

Bathing the Baby

Bathing your baby doesn't have to be more frequent than about twice a week unless there is a particularly explosive diaper. In the first few weeks, while you wait for circumcision to heal or the umbilical cord to fall off, it is best not to bathe the baby in a tub or sink. Doing so could interfere with the natural healing. Planning bath days can help reduce the risk of rashes. But bear in mind bathing is a double-edged sword. Too few baths and you risk a rash. Too many, and you risk drying out the baby's delicate skin.

Baths should be brief early on. There isn't a lot to wash anyway. This is probably best done with a washcloth and a very gentle soap — like those made for babies. Don't go hard on the soap and be sure the water temperature is lukewarm. Hot water can easily scald the baby so test it as you would with milk on your wrist or elbow. Having a plastic cup of some kind can help when rinsing the baby's hair and pouring water over the body, so the baby doesn't get cold. Go at everything gently, but wipe down all the little crevices behind the ears and the pudgy folds behind the legs. It is a good idea to clean the eyes, nose and ears, but don't use soap or anything 'clever' like Q-Tips.

If you use a baby tub, only fill it a few inches and be sure the water is off before placing the baby in the water. Leaving it running could alter the water temperature, or a distraction might find the water level too high.

When you are finished doing the simple wipe down, get the baby out of the water and into a towel to dry them off. The baby might tend to be slippery when wet — all the more reason to be extra careful. Be gentle rubbing the top of the head as the skull cap will not be fully formed and there is a soft spot. Don't press that, as the baby's delicate little brain is below. Dry the baby thoroughly. Then you might hit any areas that look red with a gentle ointment. Get that diaper on and swaddle to ensure the baby is not cold.

Dealing with Crying

One of the most challenging things about parenting a newborn is they can't tell you what they want. They sort of do, but not with words. Crying is a language, and you may get to understand how your baby is talking to you with a bit of time and patience. Babies will not all speak the same language, but you should begin to understand them after a while. A shrieking means something very different to a low-toned cry. In no particular order, crying can be due to various stressors:

- *Boredom.* Under-stimulation by being left too long alone without visual, sound or sensation of motion. The baby craves human contact and entertainment; without this, they may resort to whining as a way to self-soothe.

- *Pain.* Overfeeding can cause distension or excessive gas. It might be that the baby needs to be burped. Be sure to put on a shoulder rag if you go this route because whether the cause is too much milk or too much air, you can't predict which will come up. But there can be many sources of pain, some more or less obvious. An earache, mouth sores, urinary tract infection, constipation, or raw rash could make the baby cry out.

- *Hunger.* Probably the greatest cause of crying is hunger. In these early months the baby will need to eat often. While similar to pain in that they feel discomfort, there is one relatively easy solution to hunger, whereas pain can be trickier to resolve.

- *Needing sleep.* When your baby can't get to sleep, you may need to work on your scheduling and not let waking periods go over time—having too many visitors who want to see the baby can unintentionally trigger that. But there are also methods to calm your baby and help them enter a restful sleep.

- *Sickness.* If your baby contracts an illness and gets a fever, like you, they might have a headache and sore throat. Watch out for signs of a high fever which is considered 100.4°F/38°C. You will want to take a trip to the doctor above that temperature to find out the cause.

- *Dirty diaper.* This is probably number two on the list of uncomfortable infants. Keeping excreted matter against the skin for extended periods will make the baby uncomfortable, whether the diaper is wet or otherwise. They will let you know that they are.

- *Mother's diet.* If the mother continues to breastfeed by whatever method (pump or breast to mouth), the mother's diet may affect the child. For example, if mom consumes caffeine regularly, the child may have difficulty sleeping.

Even if her diet is mostly healthy and one or two habits don't agree with the child, there may be adverse reactions.

Other stressors may contribute to crying, but these are some of the most common causes. The list does not end there. If you really pay attention, you might learn by listening to the baby monitor what solution your baby needs. Start your diagnosis with this list.

When your baby starts crying — and it is when not if — stay calm. It is probably nothing that you are doing wrong. It will probably be frustrating, especially if it goes on for an extended period of time. You may need to put the baby down and let them cry while you go into another room and breathe. But there are methods you can find that work.

It is always good to check the simple things first, like hunger and their diaper. These are the easiest to fix. But think before jumping to any conclusions. For example, the problem is probably not hunger if the baby was just fed. After checking the diaper, it is perhaps best to consider burping even if you already did it. This does more than one thing as it comforts the baby in the stomach to chest body contact. If the baby is already with you, it is probably not boredom. They probably need to sleep if they have been up for an unusually long time.

What I am saying is keep a list (even if it is in your head) and start by eliminating what the problem shouldn't be. Take note of the things that work in solving the issue when you get the baby to stop crying and be ready to use them again. One method will probably not work the same way every time, but there are a lot of potential solutions to consider. Two of the best are motion and sound or even a combination.

Motion

Motion can successfully calm a baby — especially if you don't know the source of the issue —. Taking the baby out for a walk in the stroller can often soothe savage tantrums. I discovered by accident that walking in a gravel parking lot calmed my eldest when I tried to take a shortcut. The ride was a little bumpy, but I am betting the white noise of the stones grinding under the tires also helped get her to sleep. I put that solution in my pocket and used it often. Hopefully, the neighbors don't complain.

Strapping baby in a car seat and going on a drive is a suggestion that a lot of experts mention. The theory is that the low-frequency vibrations from the sound of the motor and wheels on the road can be soothing. Also, the baby gets moved to a different environment, there isn't a ton of stimulation in the back seat of a car, and there is a change of scenery. Even adults sometimes fall asleep from the motion of a vehicle. Just be sensible and don't go out driving when you are over-tired. In that case, it may be best to sit with the baby in a rocking chair or put it in a baby swing. The simple motion might be just the remedy to put the baby to sleep.

Noise

A popular phrase used in some households was: "Be quiet. The baby's sleeping." Mothers or fathers exhausted from getting their baby to sleep just weren't ready to have the baby wake up again. But noise can work in several different ways. Some can help you get your baby to sleep; others may cover background noise so life can go on in the household without tiptoeing around.

Music just may become your best friend—some kids like classical music and some like metal. Of course, there are lullabies and music considered to be for children. It is a bit of a trial-and-error process. Some children fall asleep or at least calm down to the sound of white noise. It sounds like turning on the shower or setting a radio to a channel that doesn't exist. Brown noise may be a better option as it is a lower frequency. Both can be useful in drowning out background noise in the house. More unusual options for sleep induction have to do with binaural beats (tone and frequency recordings). The internet offers many options for more natural noise, like rain storms. Similar to white and brown noise, the sounds of nature can be soothing for some babies.

The key to using sound or motion — or both simultaneously — is distracting the baby from the issue that is bothering them. Doing your best to diagnose the reason for crying will ultimately be the most effective way to resolve things. If the baby is already over-stimulated, it does not make sense to use a solution that will stimulate them more. If they are bored and overtired, a change in scenery might be all they need to change their mood.

Another Option for Sleep

Techniques for hypnosis can also be effective in getting babies to relax into a deep sleep. It seems they only work on babies ready to fall asleep, not those crying. Something that may be worth looking into are techniques based on Franz Mesmer's practices, developed 200 years ago. They are straightforward methods for helping your baby relax. The following is a good resource produced by an award-winning hypnotherapist. https://youtu.be/qZn6Nd0bG5k

---

Bonding with Your Baby

Making an effort to bond with your baby has a lot of benefits. First, it is necessary to begin forming your personal relationship with your new baby. Second, it can be comforting and soothing for the baby, which will help reduce crying episodes. Third, your partner will notice your effort, and that can very well enhance your relationship.

Bonding with your child begins almost immediately after birth. As it is a non-verbal process, you will not be communicating with words. You start creating your connection with touch, gesture and other physical actions. Voice does play a role, but it isn't exactly the one you may think.

The physical aspect starts with just holding your child, which is why it is essential to get comfortable. When you are uncomfortable, you subconsciously communicate with a vibe that says you are uncertain and perhaps even "I don't like this." Not the kind of message you want to begin communicating.

Your partner will have a huge advantage in her opportunities to connect with the child. She already has. Before the baby is even born, there is a connection formed through carrying the baby for nine months. But even immediately after birth, she has the chance to breastfeed, and that type of contact is something the dad will not have the opportunity to do. Well, at least not exactly.

An alternative to breastfeeding is taking the opportunity to bottle feed when that is an option. It is possible, for example, to pump breast milk and use it in bottles allowing you intermittent opportunities to feed the baby. Like your partner's first attempts at breastfeeding, bottle feeding might not go particularly well, especially if your partner is exclusively breastfeeding without a bottle. If it doesn't go well, it may work for the mom to introduce occasionally feeding with a bottle just to make the child feel comfortable with the new format. When it goes well with her, chances are that the dad has a greater probability of being able to pull it off.

Feeding is just one example of making the child accept and bond with you. It is not the be-all-and-end-all.[3] Even if the bottle feeding does not go well right away, you can take the time to practice holding the child in comforting ways. The better you get at assuming a position of nursing (cradling for bottle feeding), the more likely you will succeed with the bottle. But you will want to practice other positions, like chest-to-chest contact. You can practice making the baby feel safe in your arms during these sessions. You might even try some gentle massaging and stroking.

Another way to enhance the connection with your newborn is to talk. You don't have to use words, light singing, cooing or even humming will serve the purpose. Any vocal sounds that will help get the baby used to hearing your voice can help you make this type of connection. But there is also no reason you can't tell the child stories,

---

[3] An interesting study on the subject of bonding was a series of experiments conducted by psychologist Harry Harlow in 1958 on rhesus monkeys. In part of the series of experiments, Harlow separated newborns from their mothers and placed them with two surrogate mothers. One of the mothers was made of wire and provided only food. The other was wrapped in something like fur, which the monkeys could 'cuddle'. The infant monkeys spent more time with the cuddly mom than the one that fed them. It is worth looking at the study. https://www.simplypsychology.org/harlow-monkey.html

read books with them, or tell them about the world around them as you take them on a stroll. You will just want to be mindful of not startling the baby with a booming voice, or you may set off a crying session. But the point here is that familiarity brings comfort, trust, and bonding.

Basic care of your baby has to do as much with paying attention to your needs as well as the child's. Stepping up to go the extra mile and evolving your efforts with time makes you more inclusive in the family. The whole experience may be new to you, but this chapter should have provided some perspective on the very basics of caring for the child and making yourself welcome in their lives. You should know how to avoid grave errors, change a diaper, bathe the baby, deal with crying, and make attempts to start bonding. Of course, this is just a starting place, as your experience has to be felt out with some trial and error.

We touched on feeding here, and there is a bit more to it. That is why we look at feeding in more depth in Chapter 3.

Dad Hacks From Chapter 2

Basic Care Hack #1: Handle With Care. Just like shipping a rare vase, handling your baby should be done with the utmost care. Make sure to support your baby's head and neck every time you pick them up. If you have to bend down, make sure to bend your knees and pull the baby close to your chest.

Basic Care Hack #2: Soothing and Bonding Go Hand-in-Hand. Bonding with your baby helps them feel safe around you, and will teach them to seek you out when they feel in danger. Try different methods of soothing your baby while holding them close; all babies are unique, and your child may need to be calmed down with a variety of methods.

Basic Care Hack #3: Practice Your Diaper Change to Save Time. Like a one-man formula one pit crew, you'll want to get your diaper changing down to a science. Practice your technique, and take every opportunity to give your partner a break by changing diapers yourself. Not only will they appreciate it, but you'll be able to get faster at the change and save yourself time.

Basic Care Hack #4: Don't Let Crying Get to You. It's okay to get frustrated when your baby won't stop crying. Take a second, give yourself a moment outside with some silence (provided your partner can watch the baby), then go back in and find out the reason for their crying. Babies can cry because they are hungry, tired, have a dirty diaper, are adjusting to temperature, need to burp, and a million other reasons. Try to find your baby's frequent cry triggers and act accordingly to fix the problem.

Basic Care Hack #5: It's Okay To Call the Doctor. Some people worry they will be bothering their doctor, but anxiety in the first few months can be overwhelming. Don't hesitate to contact your doctor if you believe there are any problems at all with your baby. Yes, that means on occasion you will go in and they will say "they just have gas" or "they have a very slight fever." But it's better to be safe than sorry, and checking will help you sleep easier at night!

Chapter 3

How to Feed Your Baby the Right Way

"Nourishment comes in many forms. So does happiness." — *Ranjani Rao*

Nutrition is not something that simply satiates hunger. For your baby to grow in mind and body, develop properly, and set the stage for a healthy life, you need to feed your baby correctly. They obviously will not make any choices for themselves, so this is your responsibility. They may be able to turn on the alarm and cry when hungry, but they won't even know what they want, let alone understand what the practical options are. Baby is not going to be in the highchair throne chomping steak or wielding the handle of a turkey leg like Henry VIII anytime soon (although they will command the attention of the room like they are holding court before long).

In this chapter, we look at the idea of schedules for eating during the baby's first year and the dos and don'ts as far as what you should allow to pass their lips during their stages of development. It is good enough to tackle the basics in the beginning, to get by as you settle into a routine. You will have certain rules to follow for health and safety. But as your parenting skills increase, so should your approach to nutrition.

What's on the Menu

It probably seems impossible to an adult how little sustenance your baby actually needs in the first weeks of life. It is not more by volume than you can fit into one mouthful of your chosen drink. That volume is per feeding. This may make you wonder about the initial fuss over getting breastfeeding right because nothing much is being consumed anyway. The small initial volume is part of the reason why it isn't urgent to get it right the first time. But the need for frequency (about ten times a day) is why it is essential to work at solving any problems right away.

When the baby was in utero, they were getting nurtured constantly. Now, with a stomach about the size of a marble, they have to start to be at least partly responsible for their own subsistence (they must at least swallow). They really should not go more than four hours without feeding. While their stomach will increase in size fairly rapidly — probably quadrupling in capacity in the first two weeks — that is still just about two fluid ounces per feeding.

Expected Milk Intake by Average (Feeding and Frequency)

  Newborn to 2 weeks: .5 to 2 oz. (on demand)

  2 weeks to 2 months: 3 oz. (8X per day)

  2 to 4 months: 5 oz. (7X per day)

  4 to 6 months: 6 oz. (7X per day)

  6 to 12 months: 8 oz. (6X per day)

  12+ months: 8+ oz. (4X per day)

Keep in mind that these are ballpark numbers. You will have to adjust to your baby (e.g. If your baby is very small, the intake will be less). The whole schedule and list of expectations may be tossed on its head should your baby be born prematurely.

Choices about breastfeeding, using breast milk, or bottle-feeding with formula are personal. However, the choice to do one or the other is not always driven by a simple selection. Some factors can filter into the equation that may be beyond your control. Either way, making an informed choice means knowing why you'd select one over the other in the first place.

One curious fact about your baby and liquids is that baby should only be consuming breast milk or formula for the first year. Juice, cow's milk and even water are not recommended as they do not provide the right nutrients and won't be helpful to the baby's health and development, which are critical concerns — especially in the first year. You will be introducing solids sometime around the sixth month. There is no need to rush to that, and you will continue feeding milk/formula when the solids are introduced.

Whatever you do, pay attention to the recommendations of your pediatrician. The information here is a rough guide and not the ultimate one.

Breastfeeding

One of the tricky things about breastfeeding is you have no idea how much the baby is supping per feeding. You can be assured it isn't much in those first two weeks, and most people will find early bottle feeding not worth the effort. However, not everyone has the same interest in continuing to breastfeed or in choosing breastfeeding at all.

Before talking about bottle feeding, there are some benefits of breastfeeding over the long term to mention. Breast milk is nature's natural nectar. Evolution provides mom with the best factory for providing nutrition to her baby. Mom's milk churns out with the perfect balance of nutrients from fats and protein, plus the fluid is packed with easily digestible vitamins, trace elements and antibodies. The only caveat here is that the quality of the milk depends on the mother's diet. A well-balanced diet that limits junk food and promotes good nutrition delivers the fuel the body needs to manufacture infant-nourishing milk.

Breast milk will be easier for the baby to digest than formula. It will be supportive of all systems and functions, supportive of healthy development, and the baby will get a steady stream of beneficial bacteria to develop their intestinal flora. The nutritional benefits help boost a baby's immune system and lower the likelihood of developing allergies, ear infections and gastrointestinal issues. No matter how well 'formulated', formula doesn't do all these things. Starting your child with the ultimate food source can prepare your child for a long, healthy life. As long as mom takes a little care with what she is ingesting, there are clear nutritional benefits. Don't smoke, drink, or overdo things (e.g., caffeine, herbal supplements, fish with high mercury content, or highly processed foods).

Breast milk is always ready at the perfect temperature and in the ideal volume in the ultimate juice box. There is no need to head off to the kitchen, worry about cleaning bottles, and potential problems with 'food management' (things don't keep in the fridge forever) or sterilization. Baby takes what baby wants, and there is virtually zero waste. It is free.

One more little consideration is the benefit for mom. Milk production burns calories. The weight gained during pregnancy (all women gain during pregnancy) will be lost much faster. There are also other health benefits that may be worth researching, such as a lowered chance of developing diabetes and breast or cervical cancer.

Bottle Feeding

While the benefits of breastfeeding seem evident, there are some valid reasons why a new mom might choose to go to formula quickly — or even immediately. Bottle feeding is not necessarily independent of breastfeeding as some women may choose to pump and store their milk for bottle feeding just for the convenience of not having to always be the one responsible for the feeding. But for the sake of simplicity, 'bottle feeding' in this section refers to formula.

Some matters of convenience or practicality have people choose to go directly to bottle feeding. Not all of them are selfish or ill-advised, and they may not be steering away from what is best for the baby despite the numerous advantages of breast milk.

In rare cases, children are born lactose intolerant, which would have essentially been fatal before the availability of formula. Parents can consider substitutes, like soy milk, to bottle-feed the baby. Whether the choice to bottle-feed has a medical basis or not, bottle-feeding allows the responsibility of feeding to be shared between parents far more easily. This can help the dad bond with the child during feedings from a very early stage in a way that isn't otherwise possible. The responsibility is also not limited to the parents so that a village can help raise the child if needed.

Feeding with formula will tend to leave your baby full longer. This is partly because formula will be more difficult to digest, so it stays in the stomach longer. This comes along with the benefit of less frequent feedings. It could lead to increasing the baby's stomach capacity at a faster rate which in turn leads to needing to feed more per feeding and possibly enhanced weight gain.

Bottle feeding can be done anywhere, whereas breastfeeding can sometimes be a little awkward — no matter how normal it should otherwise be. Some cultures (e.g., the USA) will have more issues with open breastfeeding. Bottles also make it easier to measure how much your baby consumes. This also separates any concern about what mom is ingesting. Sometimes mom's personal situation can mean choosing a bottle. For example, if the mother needs treatment for a condition with medications. Medications will leech into the milk production and dose the infant as well.

Sanitation of baby bottles is critical. You want to make an effort to keep to hospital standards without dousing everything in chemicals, as chemicals do more harm than good. Optimally, you want to clean bottles immediately after you have finished using them so nothing has the opportunity to crust inside. Avoid making silly mistakes like using an old smelly sponge to do the 'cleaning.' Use a bottle brush and wash the bottles thoroughly with hot water (boiling all the bottles for regular sterilization is a good idea). Clean your bottle brush after each use as well. Read the manufacturer's instructions for proper care of your specific product.

The bottles are not the only place you need to sanitize. Regardless of what you think of your water source, you need to boil the water before mixing formula. Boil it and let it cool. While it isn't an issue if you mix bottle-by-bottle by shaking in the bottle itself, pay attention to the utensils you use to make the formula. For example, if you use a kitchen utensil to mix formula for the day (perhaps a whisk or a spoon), sterilize it beforehand by making sure it is clean and then boil the end in water for 2 minutes. Things can look clean, but it is not the things you can see that you are necessarily worried about. Err on the side of safety. Boiling water takes care of a lot of concerns. Be careful around boiling water, and don't bring the baby anywhere near it.

Introducing Solids

A few things are rough markers for when your baby is ready to start with solid foods. It could be as early as four months, but it will depend on various factors. At the very least, the baby must have good motor control of their head. They should have had good weight gain on their fluid diet (e.g., 50% weight gain from birthweight or more), and they might be showing an interest in food (reaching for solid food sources or watching intently as you eat). Other signs might include fist chewing and an increase in milk requests.

Once you decide to introduce solids, or when the doctor recommends it, plan to go slowly. Some basic warnings will help keep you out of trouble and your baby out of harm's way. Things that seem harmless additions to the baby's diet might be more like feeding chocolate to your dog. A dog will gladly take chocolate, just like your baby will start putting nearly anything in their mouth. It will not end well for the dog and could potentially kill them. You can figure out what I am inferring about the baby.

Few foods are banned from the infant's menu except for honey. Even dipping a finger in some honey to give your baby a taste of the yummy magic you may be using for its health benefits can wind up giving your child a case of infant botulism. If that sounds frightening, it should because complications can be life-threatening. The other potential source of this deadly toxin (botulinum is produced by clostridium botulinum) may include home-canned foods. It is a good reason not to feed your baby any well-meaning gifts of homemade baby foods, no matter how much you respect the person giving you the gift. While it may be impolite to refuse the gesture, utilizing them will probably be unwise and possibly life-threatening.

Along this line of thinking about foods with potentially harmful bacteria would fall any number of unpasteurized foods. These can contain even low levels of bacteria that an older child will just shrug off but still enough to infiltrate your baby's delicate immune system and create a bad situation. These same foods will be fine when that immune system is better established, but let it get established and until then, exercise caution. A good example of foods that seem harmless is cheese made with unpasteurized milk. This can easily sneak by you because most people think cheese is cheese. While most of these unpasteurized foods may be ultimately harmless, there is no reason in the world to take that risk when there are other safe choices. And, yes, this ultimately means you are going against the mantra of avoiding processed foods because pasteurizing is processing. However, you are generally turning toward foods processed specifically for infants' consumption, not the type of processed foods that get slammed by the media.

Foods with sugar and salt: both get a no. You may feel like you want the baby to experience culinary delights, but there is plenty of time for that. Salt can work against a baby's delicate metabolism and cause kidney damage. That is indeed frightening, especially when it is totally unnecessary to flavor their food. Avoiding sugar and any type of sweets for at least the first two years of development can save your baby from future health problems (there is a long list, including obesity, heart disease, high blood pressure, etc.). There is absolutely no reason the baby needs sugar in its diet. You might feel you want to give them a treat, and chances are they probably won't even like it because it may be overpowering. If they do, you may create a monster. It will be enough for them to get used to the sensation of having something other than fluid in their mouth.

One keyword to think about when it comes to your baby's diet: is bland. Imagine the scenario you are dealing with. Your baby has had nothing but air and milk until you go to introduce solid food. Getting used to swallowing solid food will be hard enough. Experiencing the invasion of a foreign substance into their oral cavity for the first time will be enough of a surprise. The reaction will probably be along the lines of electrifying their tongue and taste buds as they've been sleeping along on the same menu and flavors for six months or so. Taste buds are going to get their first test drive, and it won't take much to over-excite them. Go ahead and taste whatever it is you choose to give your baby first. It will be mushy and bland, and you probably won't like it. That's perfect.

Choking hazards are something to keep in mind. Anything that would typically require chewing is not a good idea to feed the baby. A key clue you should note is the baby's distinct lack of teeth. No teeth, no chewing. No chewing raises the choking hazard. People insist on making bad choices when it comes to this, like giving a baby a peanut. The baby is not an elephant, and your house is not a zoo. Don't do that. There are even soft foods that are not a particularly good idea. For example, jello, often considered a kid's favorite, is not for babies. They don't have to chew it as it will eventually melt in their mouth, but that's not the problem. The problem is that while it is in solid form, it can easily slide into their throat and stop the baby from breathing. That's a pretty serious consequence. It also puts aside the fact that jello is loaded with sugar, which you were already supposed to be avoiding. Donuts, no. Cakes, no. Everything needs to be mashed and sloppy — sometimes even what may seem like unpleasant slurry.

What you choose as a first food is less important than that it is simple, and the baby gets the idea of how the mechanism works. Try feeding solids for the first time before giving them a bottle. They will be more hungry at this time and willing to do more to quell that hunger. You should not force the baby's mouth open. If you take the usual path and get some kind of branded puree bland vegetable mush, get it on the spoon and let the baby offer by opening their mouth. Some pretty hysterical things can happen here, depending on the level of interest the baby has shown up to this point. They have likely been watching you eat, and mimicking is one of their preferred behaviors. If the baby isn't showing an interest as you proffer the mush on a spoon, show them how it is supposed to work. If they go to grab the spoon, let them guide it but don't let go. They might just grab what's in the spoon. Oh, well. You can't expect early attempts to go well or the mess to be contained. You can't guarantee that any will go in their mouths, either.

In the initial attempts, how much the baby eats is unimportant. They will still primarily get all their nutrition from formula/milk. You are working on creating a gateway to weaning. It does not happen all at once by any means. And really, you should only try once a day until there is progress. You may have to try this many times before it seems genuinely successful. You can meter success by the fact that something goes in and it doesn't come back out. Once the swallowing mechanism is mastered, you can start to vary the menu. There is no reason to rush and go too fast to a broad menu as there is no culinary demand from the baby. Every new food is an adventure.

Stay with mushy things. You might even let baby join in with a family meal by giving them mushy something. For example, if you are serving potatoes, let the baby have a little of it mashed. As the baby progresses, try giving them soft foods cut into small pieces. Once they handle that, give them things that are slightly more challenging. Plain Cheerios are a popular motor-skill builder. It is as simple as setting your baby up in a high chair and scattering a few Cheerios on the baby's tray. Letting them fuss and strain isn't cruel entertainment; it is helping them develop motor skills and hand-eye coordination.

Your confidence is as important as the baby's in handling what you give them. There is no real reason to hold them back from exploration as long as you are smart about the dietary choices. Keep things simple, flavor nothing, and bite sizes appropriate to their skills. Do experiment with soft foods like fresh fruits (e.g., banana, avocado), and roll out challenges a little at a time. Gradually move up to sizes baby can hold in their fist and bite off as they please.

Food Safety and Storage

To be sure that you do not create food hazards, be cautious about how you store food that your baby will be eating. If you buy baby food, check the cap on the jars before opening it by pressing the button on the lid down to check the seal. This helps you be sure that the jar didn't get opened previously in the store and that the content is not going bad (harmful bacteria can create gas, and the seal will become unstable). Once you open the jar, make sure it gets back in the fridge as soon as possible and plan to keep it for two days maximum.

There is no reason why you can't cook for a baby, but you need to be absolutely sure of your food safety practices. Anything you are cooking should be thoroughly cooked and well-cooled; when it comes to baby, think of pizza burning the roof of your mouth for everything more than slightly warm to the touch. Refrigeration is important, but you can make things worse by not doing it correctly. If you store food covered with plastic wrap or covered Tupperware, it should be cooled to 70° F/21° C before covering, or you create an environment for bacteria to thrive. Do not be casual with food safety practices, especially in the early going.

Much Ado About Water

You will not give your baby plain water in the first six months. They get all the hydration they need from their staple liquid diet. The other side is that giving them water early will deprive them of essential nutrition. Water will take up space they need for optimal nutrition.

At about six months, giving your baby small amounts of water as a stop-gap, a curiosity, and a learning tool is ok. This should always be cooled boiled water to ensure no chance of doing more harm than good, at least until the baby turns the corner at 12 months and the serious safety precautions can come off the table. Note that it says 'cooled'. Even if you boil it before refrigeration, ice water may be a bit of a shock. Your baby will not be able to describe 'brain freeze' to you, but their delicate system will be susceptible.

If you are concerned about hydration, a great barometer that will chase you throughout infancy is the number of wet diapers the baby has per day. If there are at least six reasonably wet diapers per day, your child is getting enough fluid. If it dips below there and your baby is maintaining its regular intake of milk/formula, you can consider offering water as a secondary source of hydration.

Juice becomes possible after 12 months, but the selection should be made with care. Most consumer juice products have a ton of sugar — which you want to avoid. Those that don't have chemical sweeteners (e.g., saccharine, high fructose corn syrup, sorbitol). Just because it doesn't say 'sugar' on the label — and it might even claim to be sugar-free — doesn't mean there aren't other harmful things mixed in to please the taste buds of average consumers. If you go the route of juice, stick with fresh orange juice or vegetable juices you make yourself by cooking fresh vegetables and pureeing them. Dilute any new introduction at first. If you do something silly like giving baby cabbage juice, the gastric distress may lead to hours of screaming and crying.

If your baby gets a fever, it is best to return to a strict and rather boring regimen of breast milk or formula. You may need to make feeding more frequent and expect the baby to take less volume each time. When sick, the baby will do far better on proven nutrition than with what will end up being less sustaining liquids.

***

Food is one of the basic necessities that deserves a deeper treatment. Sticking to advice that helps you keep things simple, sterile and progressive is definitely the best for the baby and probably you as well. The need for variety is not over-rated as it will teach your baby not to be too fussy about what gets put on their plate.

With nutrition under baby's belt, sleep is another big topic you must be concerned with for the baby's health and your own. Although we have covered some of the significant parts of the topic already, the next chapter rounds out the finer points of your baby's sleep regimen, so that night times go more smoothly.

Dad Hacks From Chapter 3

Feed Hack #1: Following a Schedule Can Reduce Stress. Setting up a schedule and adhering to it can take a lot of the guesswork out of feeding, helping alleviate stress that may be hindering both you and your partner. Set a timer between feedings to help you remember, though make sure the chime isn't too abrasive. No one wants to hear a blaring siren every 2 to 3 hours.

Feed Hack #2: It's Okay to Bottle Feed Occasionally. While there are some risks to bottle feeding, including the possibility of choking, ear infections, and tooth decay, it's okay to bottle feed from time to time. Bottle Feeding can give your partner's nipples a break and still give your baby the nutrients they need. Just make sure that the bottle is clean, and the baby never has it in their bed!

Feed Hack #3: No Water for the First 6 Months. It seems counterintuitive, but your baby should not have water during the first six months of their life. Baby's get all the nutrients and hydration they need from breastmilk and formula; giving them water can make them less thirsty for milk, which can stunt their growth. Even on hot days (where you should be keeping your baby inside anyway) milk is all they need.

Feed Hack #4: There Will Be Foods Your Baby Hates. Once your baby switches to solids, there is one unfortunate fact to face: they will simply despite certain types of food. Try a variety of baby foods, and see if you can get a couple in rotation they enjoy. While you'll want to teach them later about the importance of trying new foods, the most essential thing in the first year is getting them the nutrients they need.

Feed Hack #5: Watch for Choking Hazards. You would be surprised at what qualifies as a choking hazard for your baby, and you'll want to keep your eyes (and carrots) peeled when watching out for potential choking danger. Even things like corn kernals, cherry tomatoes, and pieces of vegetables can choke your baby. Remember: food pieces larger than one half an inch (width or length) can cause your baby to choke.

Chapter 4

How to Help Your Baby Sleep

Sleep; babies need it, and parents wish they could have it. Unfortunately, only one of you will likely be getting proper rest, as studies have shown that new parents only get between 5 and 6 hours of sleep a night. But for your baby, losing sleep doesn't just mean being a bit irritable and needing an extra cup of tiny coffee. Sleep is the foundation of a baby's health; without proper rest, infants can suffer from problems later in life like:

- Decreased Brain Development
- Learning and Cognition Issues
- Frequent Negative Emotions
- Problems with Growth
- More Frequent Illness

It's estimated that a baby will wake up every two to three hours to feed, meaning that your sleep schedule will be somewhat erratic in the first few months of parenthood. Understanding the exact nature of these sleep patterns and how they change as the baby grows can help you overcome these nocturnal challenges (not to mention help you hold on to your sanity during the stress that sleeplessness can bring including not being able to binge watch Netflix! Or watch my favourite cat and dog videos on social media) I certainly struggled with this during those initial months with our first child, but over time, I learned effective ways to help our baby get the essential rest it needed. It may seem like an insurmountable challenge at first, but fortunately, there are a number of techniques you can use to make this process easier. We'll start by looking at the type of sleep patterns your baby will have during those first twelve months.

Understanding Infant Sleep Patterns

How your baby sleeps will change dramatically over the first twelve months of its life; we can separate this time into three distinct stages.

Stage 1: 0-3 Months

From that first night in the hospital to the first few months at home, a baby in its first three months of life will sleep for the majority of the day. Unfortunately, this sleep is rife with irregular patterns, and as much as parents would love to get some shut-eye themselves, babies won't always be tired at night. In any given 24-hour period, a baby less than three months old will sleep between 14 and 17 hours. Waking up every two to three hours to feed, it's not uncommon for a baby to wake up shortly after getting to sleep. Babies will nap frequently throughout the day, followed by a longer night-time sleep (if you are lucky!) The baby will also move around in their sleep, making small noises and even twitching. Their breathing can become irregular; fortunately, this is entirely normal, and there is no reason to respond unless the baby wakes up.

To sum up sleep patterns in the first three months:

- Your baby will sleep between 14 to 17 hours within a 24-hour period.
- The baby will wake up every two to three hours to feed.
- Babies at this stage do not have regular sleep patterns, so prepare for them to take several naps throughout the day.
- Babies are often in a stage of rest called "active sleep." They will move, twitch, make small noises like grunts, and even wake up briefly before returning to a quieter sleep stage.

Stage 2: 3-6 Months

After the first three months, the amount of sleep a baby needs will reduce slightly. In a 24-hour period, your average infant will rest between 12 to 16 hours, which includes periodic naps throughout the day. They will still need to be fed often and will wake up every few hours to satisfy their hunger. Luckily, their sleep cycle will start to become a bit more regular. They'll spend less time in active sleep (where they are twitching, moving, or grunting) and more time in the quiet rest we associate with deep sleep. They will also (thankfully) sleep for longer at night, staying awake longer during the day.

To sum up sleep patterns between months three and six:

- Your baby will sleep between 12 and 16 hours within a 24-hour period.
- The baby will still wake up every few hours to feed.
- Babies do have a more regulated sleep pattern during these months, staying awake during the day and sleeping longer at night.
- More time will be spent in quiet sleep rather than active, so your baby will move around and twitch far less than it did during the first three months.

Stage 3: 6 to 12 Months

During months six to twelve, your baby will maintain that 12 to 16-hour-a-day sleep pattern. They'll continue to take naps during the day, though these will decrease in frequency. Instead, your baby will nap for longer stretches, marked by less activity and more quiet sleep. A baby's sleep schedule becomes far more normalized during this time, and while they will still wake up at night to feed, they will do so more often during the day. Overall, you'll deal with far less sleep disturbance on your end, and more consistent, dependable sleep will occur.

To sum up sleep patterns between months six and twelve:

- Your baby will continue to sleep between 12 and 16 hours within a 24- hour period.

- The baby will still nap during the day, though far less frequently.
- Your baby will have much quieter sleep than the active sleep that causes them to twitch and move.
- Your baby will sleep more consistently at night, though they will still need to wake up occasionally to feed.

How Can I Be Sure My Baby Has Healthy Sleep?

Much like it is to adults, sleep is essential to maintaining your baby's good health. Understanding what constitutes healthy sleep patterns and identifying the signs of poor rest can help ensure your baby's development is not harmed during these crucial first months. First, you'll want to understand what it looks like when your baby needs more rest.

Signs That Your Baby Is Tired:

• Having trouble getting settled	• Tightening its fists
• Frequently yawning	• Jerking or moving around uneasily
• Rubbing their eyes	• Quiet while awake for long periods of time
• Crying, fussing, or visibly grimacing	• Not interested in playing

If you see one or more of these signs, it may be time to deploy a couple of sleep-improvement strategies. Babies need time to develop a healthy circadian rhythm, where they are mostly awake during the day and mostly asleep during the night. Even though this rhythm will take a bit to establish itself, there are a couple of ways you can accelerate the process.

Healthy Sleep Tips:

- *Natural Sunlight:* Humans are naturally attuned to sunlight, and studies have shown that our circadian clocks respond primarily to the presence of light and dark. When your baby wakes up in the morning, make sure to open up the blinds and expose them to as much natural sunlight as possible. Similarly, ensure that the room they sleep in is as dark as possible. These two light settings can help your baby develop their rhythm as early as possible when used in tandem.
- *Rock-a-Bye Baby:* It can be difficult for a fussy baby to drift off to sleep, especially if they had a particularly stimulating day. You can help ease your baby into their sleep schedule by soothing them with gentle rocking. Other techniques that can make your baby a bit more sleepy include night-time feeding, singing to them softly, quietly shushing them as they fuss, or patting them as they begin to drift off.
- *Establish a Calming Routine:* Because we are trying to establish a rhythm, structuring bedtime around a routine can help your baby subconsciously know when it's time to go to sleep. Create a calming nightly ritual with activities like bath time, reading them a story, gentle massage, or the rocking/sleeping mentioned above. Keep this routine consistent, and before long, your baby will start to get tired before the routine has even finished.

Helping your baby nap can be accomplished with similar techniques, though the routines should be much shorter. For example, a short story or small snack before a nap can help your baby sleep more quietly, as well as putting them in the same spot (i.e. their crib) when it's time for them to rest.

Common Sleep Problems and How to Solve Them

Much like people of any other age, it's common for babies to have issues with sleeping from time to time. Different problems will occur at various times during infancy, and it can be frustrating when you aren't sure how to identify or deal with a specific issue. To figure this out, let's bring those stages from the earlier part of this chapter back and talk about a few of the sleep issues you'll face. Then, I'll show you the best way to deal with them so your baby (and you) can get some much needed shut-eye.

Sleep Problems in Stage 1: 0-3 Months

Issue: Back-Sleep Resistance

The safest way for a baby to sleep is on its back, but many infants will resist this positioning in an effort to get comfortable. Your baby will most likely prefer to sleep on his or her stomach, but studies have linked this sleeping position to higher instances of sudden infant death syndrome or SIDS.

How to Solve This Issue: To be as cautious as possible, the first step you should take is to talk to your paediatrician. It's possible that your baby may have some physical issue that is preventing it from back-sleeping comfortably; if that's the case, it should be addressed as quickly as possible. This may sound worrying, but it's just a precaution. More likely than not, your baby just doesn't feel secure sleeping on its back. If the doctor gives you the all-clear, you can encourage back sleeping by swaddling your baby and giving them a pacifier. These, and other comforting elements like reading to them at bedtime or feeding them before sleep, can make your baby feel secure in a back-sleeping position.

Issue: Difficulty Establishing a Circadian Rhythm

It's common for infants to mix up night and day when they are first born, sleeping while the sun is up but becoming active come nightfall. While it may be easy to think, "well, hey, any sleep is good sleep!" Unfortunately, this can make it much more challenging to establish a healthy rhythm later. Not only that, but most parents sleep during the night, so being up all night and all day with your baby can take a toll on your physical and mental health.

How to Solve This Issue: While your baby will most likely grow out of this pattern of sleeping all day and partying all night, there are ways to fix this rhythm early. Make sure that your baby associates sunlight with wakefulness. This can be done by either introducing natural light into their room in the morning or moving them to a sunlit room shortly after they wake. You also want to reduce your baby's blue light exposure during the day. For example, if you watch TV with your baby in the room, make sure to turn it off before the sun goes down.

Issue: Restlessness After Night Feedings

Your baby will frequently wake up during the first three months to feed, filling their bellies one, two, and even three times a night to get the nutrients they need. For some babies, this stimulation can cause them to struggle when trying to go back to bed. This problem only worsens as the night gets on, as a baby who has just fallen back asleep and quickly wakes up again to eat will undoubtedly be fussier.

How to Solve This Issue: All babies are unique, and your infant may be feeding too often at night. Overfeeding can often cause sleeplessness, and if the time between these feedings is shorter due to being awake, your baby won't get the rest it needs. The solution is to feed them less often, but you'll want to visit your paediatrician to discuss this before changing their feeding schedule. If they approve, you will likely increase their daytime feedings and stretch out the time between night-time feedings so they can get proper rest.

Sleep Problems in Stage 2: 3-6 Months

Issue: Sleep Regression

It's possible for the first few months of your baby's sleep to seem to progress and improve, only for a sudden drop to occur around the 3-4 month mark. This is called sleep regression, and it may happen every few months. During sleep regression, the times your baby used to get tired changes dramatically, and they will be far more awake or active at inconvenient times. Your baby may even appear to be fighting the urge to sleep and will wake up more often once they drift off.

How to Solve This Issue: While it may seem counterintuitive, sticking to the same routine that your baby is resisting is often the best way to break through sleep regression. Whatever your usual night-time ritual is, whether that be a pre-bed feed, nightly bath, storytime, or gentle lullabies, it should be kept in place. You can also supplement the time your baby loses during night-time regression occurrences by increasing the number of naps they have during the day. Remember, sleep regression is a temporary phenomenon. Push through, and your baby will be back on their regular sleep schedule in a few days or weeks.

Issue: Changes in Nap Schedule

Babies will progressively nap less throughout their first year of life, and this usually translates to longer stretches of sleep during the night. On the other hand, if your baby is napping less but showing signs that they are tired or struggling to sleep at night, they may need to nap more to get the sleep they need.

How to Solve This Issue: You can encourage your baby to nap by going through a routine similar to the one you use at night. While mimicking your bedtime routine, this nap routine will be much shorter, but it should still be effective in letting your baby know it's time to rest. A good example would be if you have a decent bit of storytime before bed and read a short story before a nap. Eventually, this irregularity should correct itself, but in the meantime, it's important your baby naps as much as they need to.

Sleep Problems in Stage 3: 6-12 Months

Issue: Can't Get Back to Sleep on Their Own

Much like adults, babies may wake up during the night for no real reason at all. At this stage, they will usually drift back to sleep on their own, and learning how to do so is a necessary habit for them to develop as they age. On the other hand, If a baby between six and twelve months needs to be fed or rocked to sleep each time it wakes up, that may signal they are having a problem with their sleep patterns.

How to Solve This Issue: If your baby is having trouble falling asleep independently, you may want to do a bit of sleep training. This means establishing a good bedtime routine and noting what behaviour's usually encourage your baby to fall asleep quickly. You will want to place your baby in the spot where they typically sleep, giving them a way to self-soothe in case they wake up. A pacifier is a great example; if your baby wakes up, they will use the pacifier to soothe themselves instead of relying on you to get them settled.

Issue: Teething Pain Disrupting Sleep

Most babies will get their first tooth by the time they are six months old, and teething pain will persist while the rest of their teeth start to grow. You will see the signs of this pain throughout the day, with biting, fussing, drooling, and general irritability being the most common indicators. Teething pain can carry on into the night, waking your baby frequently and interrupting its sleep.

How to Solve This Issue: It will be tempting to pick up and hold your baby during these teething pain spells, but you should do your best to leave them be. Too much attention will make them focus on the teething pain by associating it with receiving attention. Instead, give your baby a teething ring, and give them a few gentle pats or shushes before leaving the room. Talk to your paediatrician about medication like baby aspirin if the problem persists.

Tips for Safe Sleeping

In addition to ensuring their sleep is as restful as possible, you'll want to ensure your infant is safe during both night and naptime. There are a few guidelines you can follow to make sure their sleeping environment is the safest it can be, along with a few behaviour's you can take part in to reduce their risk of injury.

- Make sure your baby always sleeps on their back. You'll want to monitor your baby while it's sleeping until it gets into this habit, as many babies will naturally try to sleep on their stomachs.

- Keep the room at an appropriate level of darkness and within the optimal temperature range. This is usually between 68 and 72 degrees Fahrenheit, though some babies may prefer a cooler temperature.
- Use a cradle or crib that meets all safety guidelines, and ensure it has been correctly assembled. If possible, purchase your crib new; that way, you won't have to worry whether it has any pieces that have worn down or become compromised.
- Dress your baby in a fitted onesie, and make sure their crib is clear of all pillows, toys, and blankets before they sleep.
- Find a firm and flat mattress for their crib with a tight-fitting sheet, and keep the crib in the same room where you sleep for the first six months.
- Avoid bed-sharing with your infant. The safest place for your infant to sleep is in their crib, and bed-sharing can increase their risk of injury or death. If you do bed share, make sure that your bed is set to the same conditions as your baby's crib. That means a firm mattress, fitted sheet, and no blankets, pillows, or toys that could suffocate the baby.

From Sleep to Sass: Let's Talk About Your Baby's Emotions

Now that we've covered the different sleep stages your infant will go through in the first year and their associated issues, let's move on to your baby's ability to regulate their emotions. Learning self-control and developing emotional intelligence are important building blocks in your infant's growth, and starting early is always better. In our next chapter, we'll discuss what self-regulation is, why it's important, and how you can help your baby develop it in the first twelve months of their life.

Dad Hacks From Chapter 4

Sleep Hack #1: **Establish a Bedtime Routine.** Whether you read your children's stories, bath them, or sing them songs, create an activity that signals to your infant's brain that it's almost time to sleep.

Sleep Hack #2: **Use the Power of Natural Sunlight.** Exposing your infant to sunlight first thing in the morning will help them develop their circadian rhythms sooner, leading to better sleep patterns at the early stages of development.

Sleep Hack #3: **Watch for the Sleep Deficiency Signals.** If your baby is constantly yawning, fluttering their eyelids, losing interest in activities that usually stimulate them, tightening their fists, or crying more frequently, they may be sleep deprived. Identify these signs early to correct the problem and get them back into a healthy sleep pattern.

Sleep Hack #4: **Make Sure Your Baby Sleeps On Its Back.** One of the easiest ways to ensure your child's safety while they sleep is to make sure they sleep on their back. Watch your baby closely during their sleep, and turn them over whenever they start to shift to their stomach. Babies prefer stomach sleeping, but through consistent sleep training, they will learn to associate back positioning with bedtime.

Sleep Hack #5: **Find a Comfort Item.** A safe bedtime comfort item can help your baby learn to fall asleep independently and reduce the amount you need to tend to them at night. This shouldn't be a toy or blanket, as that could cause the baby to suffocate. Instead, use an item like a pacifier designed to go in a baby's mouth without harming them.

Chapter 5

How to Teach Your Baby to Develop Self-Regulation

We've all had it happen: you are eating at a restaurant, sitting at a local sports game, or walking through the mall, and no matter what you do, your baby just won't stop crying. Maybe they're upset that the restaurant doesn't have a good wine selection, perhaps they placed a large bet on the game, and their team is losing, or maybe the mall Santa that year is a bit weird and smells like old bread. Whatever the reason, it can be frustrating when your baby won't calm down. The cause for their distress is simple; they have yet to develop the ability to self-regulate their emotions.

In truth, it's very reasonable that a baby would have difficulty with self-regulation, or the ability to control one's emotions rather than act on impulse. But the sooner your baby learns this skill, the better; developing self-regulation early can help your baby later in several ways, including:

- *Learning in School:* A child that is screaming and crying in school may be removed from a classroom, causing them to fall behind in their education and miss important lessons. It's also more challenging to take in information if your emotions are getting the better of you; a well-behaved child is more likely to focus and soak up everything that school has to offer, setting them up for success as they advance in their educational career.

- *Making Friends:* No one wants to invite a mini-Godzilla to their birthday party, and an out-of-control child will face an uphill battle to find willing playmates. Socializing and making friends are essential foundational events in a baby's life, but without self-regulation, it's unlikely other children will want to play or converse with your child. By learning to take turns in games, share their toys with other children, and express their emotions in a healthy and measured manner, your baby will be more likely to form strong connections and create lasting friendships.

- *Behaving Themselves Socially:* Regulating emotions can keep a person from acting in socially inappropriate ways. For example, if your child is screaming and crying in a store, you will likely feel embarrassed and may even be asked to leave. A child without emotional self-regulation may also participate in behaviour's that could damage property or injure themselves and others. If a child is mad and doesn't know how to handle it, they may lash out physically or destroy the things around them. Teaching your child to control their emotions early can save them from the consequences of these types of actions.

- *Becoming Independent:* Developing self-regulation means that your child will understand how to calmly assess different situations and make rational, appropriate decisions on how to act. This means they will be coming to you less for guidance, which will become incredibly important later on in their lives. While a baby is naturally very dependent on their parents, emotional self-regulation is the first step in moving towards the eventual self-reliance they will have to develop.

Several different activities and events can send a baby into a negative emotional state, and without self-regulation, they will have difficulty self-soothing and becoming calm. These activities can be almost anything, including hunger between meals, a dirty diaper, unfamiliar guests, loud noises, or a strange new environment. As your child grows, they will need to learn to adapt and adjust to new experiences without giving in to their emotions or impulses. This is the basis for learning self-regulation, and while it may take years for your child to develop this skill fully, you'll want to start identifying and strengthening their ability to do so as soon as possible.

Let's start by discussing how self-regulation manifests in different stages of your baby's first year and how your infant will slowly develop these skills over time. Look for the various signals that show what emotions your baby is dealing with; that way, you can adjust your soothing strategies and help bring that back into a calm, happy state.

Self-Regulation in the First Twelve Months

So what does self-regulation look like in children? Well, it varies from month to month. As your baby's brain develops, they will learn to process and express their emotions in different ways. Every child is unique, but if we are speaking in general terms, self-regulation usually involves:

- The ability to focus on a task
- How well your baby can switch from one task to the next
- The ability to control impulses
- Not overreacting to emotions like anger, embarrassment, excitement, and frustration
- Behaving with other children and adults

In the early stages of your infant's life, it won't be easy to discern whether certain aspects of this self-regulation are happening. As your baby becomes more mobile and expressive, you should be able to see how far along their self-regulation skills have advanced.

Self-Regulation Signs: *Months 0-3*

When your baby is a newborn, it's not easy to quantify how much emotional regulation is taking place. That being said, there are a few common signs to watch for:

Sign #1: Attention Span and Spotlight

During the first three months of its life, your baby will display its level of emotional regulation largely by how it focuses on items of interest. Most infants at this stage have a very "sticky" attention spotlight; this means that if they begin to focus on something, it will be difficult to change their focus to something else. If your baby can focus on a single item of interest and has no difficulty switching to and concentrating on another item, that likely means they already have some modicum of self-regulation abilities.

Sign #2: Alertness and Sleep-Wake Patterns

One sign of poor emotional self-regulation is how your baby deals with the sleeping and waking parts of their day. The more erratic a baby's sleep schedule, the more likely they will have a tough time controlling their emotions. Now, this is completely understandable at this stage of infancy. Babies initially have erratic sleep patterns, and the subsequent trouble with self-regulation is a byproduct. However, the more you can do to regulate their sleep patterns, the more they will be able to control their emotions. Refer to Chapter 4 for ways to help your baby get the best sleep possible.

Sign #3: Behaviour Governed by Reflex and Sensation

A baby's behaviour in the first three months of their life will primarily be controlled by their reflexes and how they respond to different sensations. So if your baby feels the sensation of hunger, it will likely begin to cry. If your baby feels tired, it will also start to cry. Basically, many different sensations will activate their reflex to cry, as they don't yet possess the self-regulation tools to deal with these feelings.

Self-Regulation Signs: *Months 3-6*

During months three to six, your baby will develop stronger self-regulation skills, especially if they get proper sleep and behavioural encouragement. There are a few signs to look for that can help you determine their self-regulation in this stage.

149

Sign #1: Intentional Behaviours

One sign of increased emotional regulation you will see during this stage is more intentional behaviour's. Your baby will start to move not just around but towards particular objects. They will also reach out and grasp things that they are focusing on. The more they engage in these behaviour's, the more they develop their self-regulation abilities. You can facilitate this by giving them the freedom to move about as they like or bring objects they are focusing on close so they can grab them.

Sign #2: Increased Alertness Time

Your baby's self-regulation will increase along with their alertness time, which can manifest in a few different ways:

- *Active State:* This form of alertness involves frequent movement and changing focus, along with your baby making small audible sounds. These movements will usually follow a certain rhythm and occur in small bursts. This may be your baby simply responding to a stimulus, but it can also be a warning sign that they may soon become fussy.
- *Quiet State:* Another alertness stage involves our baby quieting down but still engaging and looking for physical interaction. Your baby may touch your face or hands and focus on the sound of your voice. There is much less movement during this stage as your baby focuses on seeing and hearing. The quiet state is the ideal precursor to drowsiness and sleep, as it symbolizes they are entering a more calm and relaxed state of mind.
- *Crying State:* Crying is a baby's reflexive response to various emotions, sensations, and stimuli, usually when they feel some type of discomfort. This usually comes in the form of hunger or tiredness. A baby in a crying state will move more aggressively, shifting their arms and legs and contouring their face into an unpleasant expression. The crying state can usually be helped by soothing your baby and identifying what issue is causing their distress.

- *Drowsy State:* Before each instance of sleep, your baby will almost always enter a state of least alertness, the drowsy state. During this time, your baby will move very little but still make certain facial expressions like smiling or frowning. They will struggle to remain focused on much of anything, with their eyes glazing and eyelids drooping. If you see your baby enter this state, it's best to move them to their designated sleeping area so they can rest.

Sign #3: More Regulated Sleep Patterns

The times your baby isn't alert, whether it be when they are asleep at night or during a nap, become far more regulated as you enter months three through six. If they remain chaotic, that will almost always reduce your baby's ability to self-regulate their emotions. If your baby is struggling to establish a solid circadian rhythm or sleep pattern, you'll want to take steps to correct it as soon as possible. Again, refer to chapter 4 for tips on how to help your baby sleep properly.

Self-Regulation Signs: *Months 6-12*

During the last six months of your baby's first year, their ability to self-regulate will expand exponentially. This will show in their ability to maintain their attention, their mannerisms, and how they perceive patterns.

Sign #1: Flexible Attention Adjustment

At this point, a good marker for your baby's self-regulation abilities is whether they can shift their attention. If a baby is flexible in how they move their focus from different people and objects to new areas of interest, that means they are keeping their emotions in check. Your baby may be unable to do this all the time, and this skill won't become fully established for the next few years. But the ability to focus on an object for a few seconds and then switch to another is an excellent sign for their emotional development.

Sign #2: Pattern Recognition

Around this stage, your baby will begin to recognize simple, repetitive patterns. These are almost always very simple, like stripes of colours, certain numbers, basic images, and shapes. Playing with toys like blocks and putting them into a recognizable pattern is a good way to build this pattern recognition skill. Recognizing patterns can also increase your baby's reasoning ability, leading to better emotional regulation later in life.

Sign #3: Movement and Mannerisms

The development of certain regulation systems will also take place during this stage, with your baby moving and acting in ways to react calmly to different sensations. For example, if your baby is feeling overstimulated and has learned to recognize when it's occurring, they will turn their head away from you (or the source of stimulation.) At the same time, babies may begin to suck their thumbs in response to stressful events. This shows they recognize when something is overwhelming them and are self-soothing to regulate their emotions.

Tips to Improve Your Baby's Self-Regulation

Two basic ways to improve your baby's self-regulation are to teach them self-control and increase their self-confidence. Here are a couple of tips you can use to do so.

Tips for Increasing Self-Control

- *Lead by Example:* While this will become more helpful later once your baby can recognize behavioural patterns, you'll want to lead by example when it comes to self-control. Don't lose your cool in front of the baby, and manage your own anger when situations become frustrating.
- *Show Them How to Act in Public:* Babies cry in public; it's an unavoidable fact of life. Whether this happens in a restaurant, grocery store, movie theatre, church, or anywhere else, make sure not to overreact. Calmly soothe your baby,

as this will teach them that this isn't the place to lose control of their emotions. You can also take them outside to remove them from the negative stimuli that may be causing their emotional reaction.

- *Establish a Routine:* Babies are more likely to learn self-control if they find comfort in a regular routine. Meals, baths, bedtime and naptime, all of these regular daily events should follow a similar path each and every day—for example, your routine at bedtime. If you feed your baby, read them a story, and then tuck them in, make sure to do this sequence of events in the same way, every night.

Tips for Increasing Self-Confidence

- *Comfort Your Baby:* Your baby will feel much more confident if it can feel safe in a calm and comforting environment. In infants, self-control mostly depends on how they self-soothe; when your baby is upset, it needs to learn how to calm itself down in case you aren't around. Their sleeping environment is an excellent example of this. Having a dark enough room to sleep in but still with soft lighting sources, as well as a comfortable crib, can help a baby calm itself down when it wakes up at night.
- *Respond to Your Baby's Needs:* Your baby will signal when it's having difficulty with certain stimuli or emotions, and you'll want to recognize these signs and respond accordingly. Whether your baby is crying, giving you a certain facial expression, or gesturing in a particular way, observe what caused this reaction and adjust your behaviour accordingly.
- *Use Positive Reinforcement:* Positive reinforcement is a great way to help your baby discern which actions are appropriate and which aren't, which can boost their self-confidence. This positive reinforcement can take many forms, including:

- A gentle high five
- Clapping
- Cheering
- Telling them, they are a cool little fella or gal (or a less goofy compliment)

- Smiling
- A thumbs-up
- Giving them their favourite toy
- Patting them on the back

Any of these actions function as effective behavioural modification and serve to encourage prosocial behaviour's. These behaviour's include following directions, eating a meal without fuss, sharing their toys with playmates, and refraining from hurting themselves, property, or others.

Making Your Baby Feel At Ease: Tune in to Their Temperament

One of the best ways to determine how your baby is dealing with their emotions is to become familiar with their temperament. Temperament is how people of any age deal with the world around them; this means overcoming challenges, managing feelings, and acting on or ignoring impulses.

There are three major components to your baby's temperament:

1. *Mood*

While it can be easy to determine an adult's mood because of their ability to vocalize their feelings, it can be much more difficult to accurately assess how a baby is feeling. Try to observe your baby's facial expressions, movements, and noises during various activities. An upset baby will usually screw up their face as though they ate something sour, balling their fists and crying to let you know they are displeased. These are more general traits, as every infant is unique; identify your baby's good and bad mood signs, then find ways to comfort them and lift their spirits.

2. *Adaptability*

Another foundational component of your baby's temperament is their ability to adapt to new situations. Learn your baby's strengths, what they excel at, and the activities they tend to struggle with. Maybe your baby is very good at sleeping in an unfamiliar location, like if you take them with you on vacation, but less adept at trying new foods. Learning their personality and what obstacles they are better suited to overcome can be incredibly helpful. You'll want to put your baby in situations they are more comfortable in on lousy mood days, then try to challenge them and get them outside of their box on their good mood days. Showing your baby how to adapt and be flexible will be very helpful later on in their lives, though it's a skill that often takes several years to internalize.

3. *Intensity*

Just as important as what situations elicit a reaction from your child is how intensely they react. When your baby is presented with a situation or sensation they don't like, do they make a face or burst out into loud sobs? If your child doesn't like a person or object, do they simply turn away or lash out physically? The intensity of your child's reactions is a very telling sign of their temperament; if they overreact to everyday situations, that's a good sign they'll need some behavioural training to improve their self-regulation.

Self-Regulation is Important, But Only One Part of the Equation

Starting early is key when helping your baby develop self-regulation, self-control, and self-confidence, but there are only some of the puzzle pieces that make up their minds. Your baby's mental state and emotional well-being are a complicated tapestry that you will need to assess and assist throughout their first year of life. In our next chapter, we'll look at how you can strengthen their emotional and mental health and the best ways to bond properly with your baby.

Dad Hacks From Chapter 5

Self-Regulation Hack #1: Provide Your Baby With Different Sensory Activities. It will be much easier to recognize your baby's emotional state and level of self-regulation if they can express themselves. By providing them with various sensory activities, you can expand the areas of their brain that allow them to make facial expressions and eventually vocalize their thoughts. A play gym is one great tool which gives infants various toys to play with to strengthen their hand-eye coordination and the muscles around the eyes. Another good sensory activity is reading to them, which stimulates the language centre in their brain.

Self-Regulation Hack #2: Track Your Child's Behaviour in a Journal. Watch your baby closely while it participates in various activities and see how it reacts to certain stimuli. Does your baby get easily frustrated? Do they play well with others and share their toys? Does your baby tend to focus on a given object of interest, and how easily can they adjust their focus? Take notes about your baby's reactions, and see how they change over time. Hopefully, your baby begins to show signs they are developing their self-regulation skills; if not, that can indicate you should do more focused behavioural training.

Self-Regulation Hack #3: Don't Be Afraid to Intervene. It's easy to worry that by intervening when your baby is upset, you could make their mood even worse. But the best thing to do when your baby reacts strongly to a sensation or emotion is to actively engage with them and try to improve their mood. Soothe your baby when they are crying, or give them a toy or object that comforts them. If they are in an overstimulating setting, like a movie theatre, take them outside until they have calmed down.

Self-Regulation Hack #4: Organize Play Dates for Your Baby. One of the most significant advantages of proper self-regulation is behaving in social situations. Without learning self-control, your baby could grow up to be a person who does not treat others well and therefore loses out on the chance to socialize with their peers properly. Organize play dates for your baby early, and watch how they interact with others. Make sure to use positive reinforcement when your baby is kind and caring to other children; at the same time, let them know when their behaviour is inappropriate. Over time, your baby will learn the correct way to act in social situations, setting them up to make friends and meaningful connections as they grow.

Self-Regulation Hack #5: Keep their Comfort Item Close. It may seem like a crutch, but it's not always possible to calm your child down with shushing and back rubs alone. At this point, you've likely identified a comfort item that your baby has fixated on. This may be a specific pacifier, toy, stuffed animal, or any other object that brings your baby comfort. Make sure this item is packed for any trip you take, even if it's just to the store or local park. Leaving your baby in an emotionally heightened state of crying or agitation isn't good for them. You'll want every tool available to you to help soothe their emotions quickly.

Chapter 6

How to Help Your Baby Develop Their Mental and Emotional Health

Caring for your baby's mental and emotional health can seem like an impossible task at times, mainly because your baby can't yet vocalize its feelings. Taking a self-care day or helping out a loved one can be as simple as drawing a calming bath with a glass of wine or taking your partner on a romantic vacation. While we all wish we could give our child a warm glass of formula or a trip to the baby Bahamas to help them recharge, the fact is that your baby will need careful guidance to grow its mental faculties. Here are some tips to help develop your infant's mental health as they grow throughout their first year.

Mental Health Tips for Each Developmental Stage in Year One

First Development Stage: Month 1-3

From the time you first get home from the hospital through the next few months, you will begin to learn about your baby's personality and attune to their feelings. I remember our first child developing their baby talk early on, and I would always light up when I heard their happy squeaking. At the same time, it was easy to recognize when our baby wasn't having a good day; their signature pout would almost always be followed by a torrent of tears and frowns. There are a couple of ways you can help your baby in those first six months when you see an impending tantrum train coming down the tracks.

Tip #1: *Engage All Their Senses*

Allowing your baby to touch, feel, hear and move about freely is all important to align their physical and mental feelings. When they are first born, your child will likely not understand the sensations of movement and touch. If you give them freedom of movement, they will slowly learn to control how they interact with the world. Make sure you have a lot of skin-to-skin contact with them as well; this can comfort your baby as it interacts with the world, making them feel more secure and confident in their exploration.

Tip #2: *Soft Tones, Smiles, and Baby Talk Time*

Positive reinforcement and communication are foundational to strengthening your baby's mental health. Much like with our child's happy squeaks, your baby will develop their own pre-language way of communicating with you. Encourage this by baby-talking back, using soft tones and smiling while you speak. Make sure to use real words with your infant, as they will start to emulate your speech and expand the language centers of their brain. You can also change the tone and volume of your voice to see how your baby reacts to changes in speech, gauging how their facial expressions and vocalizations change as your behavior shifts.

Tip #3: *Soothe and Stimulate*

Use toys like a rattle or bell to pull your baby's focus and help them move around. Moving a shiny toy in front of them up and down can help them develop their neck and shoulder muscles. If your baby becomes overstimulated, and it looks like the dark cloud of a crying storm is moving in, soothe your baby by rubbing them gently on the back. If your baby does tip over into a tantrum, pick them up and cuddle them; this will almost always help them calm down and get back to smiling and playing.

Second Development Stage: Month 3-6

At this point, your baby will start to develop better vision, and many objects will begin to take shape in their mind. By month three, it's like they've found little baby glasses they can put on, giving them more confidence and an increased desire to explore. Depending on your baby's temperament, they will still be very attached to you and your partner. Our second child was particularly devoted to their mom, and I could only get their attention by bribing them with a new rattle or shiny set of keys. Be careful with this toy bribery method though; if your baby is anything like mine was, they'll try to eat your car keys the second you turn your back!

Here are some mental health tips for months 3-6.

Tip #1: *Show Them a Variety of Photos*

At this point, your baby will start to identify shapes and colors, so you should show them a wide variety of pictures. While it may be tempting to show them those vacation pictures no one else seems interested in, it's much better to have them look at things, places, and people they may interact with in the outside world. Observe how your baby interacts with each picture, and say the name of everything they see to help establish a connection in their mind. An excellent place to start is with animals; you may even find out your baby's favorite animal before their first word! Our first child loved dolphins and would smile endlessly, looking at photos of them diving in and out of the water, leading to many future trips to the aquarium.

Tip #2: *Mirror Your Baby's Sounds and Play Games With Them*

Smile, laugh, and try to make the same faces or gestures your baby does as a way to pull their focus. This gets them to develop their facial recognition skills and helps keep them in a good mood. You can also play little games, like the classic "peek-a-boo". Hide your face behind your hands, peeking through your fingers until your baby changes their expression. Then remove your hands and exclaim (with a big smile, of course) and watch them laugh and squeal.

Tip #3: *Encourage Your Baby to Follow and Touch Safe Objects*

You'll also want to show your baby how to focus on particular objects and learn what things are safe to touch. Something like a colorful cup is a good one to start with; simply move the cup in front of their face until their eyes are clearly following it. Move up, down, left, right, then move it within their grip range. You want them to reach out and touch it, learning that it's safe to do so. Make sure it's made of a nonbreakable material though; I remember our baby grabbing my favorite mug off the table and dropping it to the floor. We were both crying that day!

Third Development Stage: Month 6-12

At six months old, your baby's exploration will reach new heights as they begin to crawl around your home. This can be both a blessing and a curse; nothing is more stressful than looking at your phone for a moment, only to look up and see that your baby has vanished into thin air. I suggested to my partner we put a bell on our child to keep track of them, but this idea was shot down. Instead, make sure you keep a close eye on them as they learn locomotion and continue finding ways to strengthen their mental and emotional health. Here are some tips for months 6-12.

Tip #1: *Words, Words, Words*

At this point, you should be saying as many words as possible to your baby, particularly their name. Your baby will learn to recognize their name and turn their head to whoever is saying it, which becomes particularly helpful when they start to crawl. You'll also want to point to places and objects, helping them associate the word with its meaning. Make sure not to speak too loudly, as this can scare them or create negative associations with whatever they interact with. Instead, smile and speak in gentle tones, putting your baby at ease and allowing them to learn in a comforting environment.

Tip #2: *Provide Your Baby With Safe, Colorful Objects*

Your baby will naturally reach out, grab, and fiddle about with anything within arm's reach, so make sure to provide safe things for them to do so with. Our first baby was particularly fond of wooden spoons, which they would bang like drumsticks onto their high chair. As long as the object is not breakable, any wooden or plastic thing should work perfectly fine. You can also give your baby simple puzzles or picture books to look at; anything that will stimulate their brain. Make sure the puzzle pieces aren't too small, or your baby may mistake them for a flavorless choking hazard to munch on.

Tip #3: *Connect Sounds to Gestures*

As your baby's brain develops, it will start to draw connections between movements and vocal expressions. Encourage this by showing the baby common expressions, like "good-bye." As someone leaves your home, wave to them while saying "bye" and then move your baby's hand. You can also do this when someone arrives, saying hello and placing your baby's hand up. This will teach them to imitate these movements and recognize the correct reactions in social situations.

How to Bond With Your Baby

While bonding with a new friend or coworker is as simple as getting a beer together, finding a mutual interest or type of music, bonding with your baby is very different. For one, your baby probably doesn't have the same taste in music (even if the Wiggles do have a couple of pretty good songs.) Bonding with a baby is more about the natural attachment, and unconditional love parents and children develop for one another throughout the first stages of life.

This process can take a few weeks to several months as the mutual love grows gradually. It's important not to panic if you don't feel that love blossoms instantly, as these emotions can take time to kick in. Pregnancy and childbirth are stressful, as is being a parent. I didn't get this bond for several months after our first child was born;

believe me, I was freaking out. But there are ways to encourage that strong, loving feeling to grow; let's talk about a few ways to help develop an emotional bond with your baby.

6 Ways to Bond With Your Baby

1. Big Smiles, Happy Talks

Studies have shown that babies can recognize smiles from an early age, and this ability only gets stronger as their eyesight improves with age. The same goes for happy speech, and while they don't yet have the ability to respond verbally, your baby will bond with you simply by smiling back and listening to you talk. They also learn the power of smiling early on, and by mirroring this behaviour back to them, you encourage them to associate smiling with feelings of happiness.

2. Funny Faces

It may seem goofy, but making funny faces to entertain your child actually enhances their ability to bond with you. Your baby will imitate the faces you make and start to recognize whether a facial expression means someone is happy or sad. As your baby learns your emotions and you learn theirs, the bond between you will strengthen. Don't be afraid to make the silliest faces possible with your child; just because it's a bit childish doesn't mean it's not helpful (and fun!)

3. Karaoke Often

Karaoke isn't just for embarrassing yourself in front of your coworkers on a Friday night; it's also great for entertaining your baby. Singing helps your baby identify your distinct voice and can even be used to establish a routine for your child's day. If you sing a song every night before bedtime, you may see your baby start to get tired before they even get to their crib. The songs don't have to be nursery rhymes either; belt out your favorite pop songs, musical numbers, or anything else. As long as you look happy and your baby smiles, your bond is stronger.

4. Dance the Day Away

In the same vein as singing, dancing is an excellent way to show your baby positive emotions and how to move around freely. It also helps relieve stress and release those feel-good hormones in your body, which can directly affect your (and your baby's) mood. Dance while your child is watching, or pick them up and carefully have them join you. This can be a soothing method when your baby is upset or tired, getting them moving and taking their mind off their discomfort.

5. Skin to Skin Contact

Skin to skin contact has been proven to relax and calm both the parent and child, lowering your baby's heart rate and giving their breathing a healthier rhythm. It can also regulate their temperature, stimulate their digestion, and interest them more in feeding. Holding your baby to your skin is an excellent bonding technique and should be done frequently, starting shortly after their birth. Simply hold contact for 30 minutes at a time in a calm and relaxed environment to avoid overstimulating your baby. In no time, you will feel a connection with your child, and they will likewise associate you with love, safety, and a feeling of calm.

6. One on One Time

Part of getting your baby to bond with you is separating yourself from other people they interact with. While many family and friends will want to visit soon after the birth, you and your partner should spend plenty of one on one time with the baby. Your child needs to become comfortable with your touch, voice, and presence; this accelerates the bonding process and helps them understand that you are their primary protector and provider.

Bonding With the Help of Baby Talk

While seemingly nonsensical, baby talk is one of the best bonding techniques you can utilize. Studies have shown that engaging a baby in normal conversation activates different sections of its brain, but baby talk causes those same parts to light up dramatically. Your baby's brain is developing rapidly in its first few years of life, forming connections and processing information that will help it learn and think. If you want to help these synapses grow quickly and bond with your baby simultaneously, you'll need to act just a little bit silly.

The best baby talk teacher you'll have is…well, your baby. They will engage you with those classic goo's and gah's, and you can emulate them. Just make sure not to interrupt your baby while they are talking. Pretending your baby is like a friend telling you a story you can't follow; nod your head politely, maintain eye contact, and let them know you are listening. Once there is a break in the conversation, respond with a mixture of similar noises and grown-up talk. All of this trains your baby's brain to identify the call-and-response nature of conversation, which will be incredibly helpful as they develop their speaking ability.

How you talk with your baby will also change over the first year. Let's break down the different stages of development and how you should engage in baby talk for each.

Month 1-3

Your infant's communication will be very limited at this stage and will usually consist of gurgles, goo's, coohs, and a baby's favorite: crying. This is accompanied by movement and smiles; observe how your baby moves and reacts to your speech, and adjust your tone and volume to elicit a happy response. For the first three months, you'll want to:

- Keep it simple. Talk, sing, and babble like your baby would, keeping the tone light and happy.
- Narrate what you are doing. While your baby won't quite be able to process it yet, saying what is happening will help them form the foundational connections between speech and action.
- After a few months, your baby will be able to make some sounds resembling words. Mimic them when they do this,

165

and say some words that include those vowel sounds. For example, if they start saying "ah", say "aeroplane."

- Start to get them in the rhythm of conversation. Let them talk, and then talk back to them when they stop.

Month 3-6

At this point, your baby will start to get the hang of copying certain sounds and even parts of words. It's even possible that they learn to control the volume of their voice, raising it if you get further away and lowering it as you get close. To encourage this development, you'll want to:

- Help them finish words that they seem to be attempting to vocalize. This is less abstract than the "aeroplane" example from the first stage; if a baby is pointing towards their bottle and saying "bah", you can say "bottle" and hand it to them.
- Ask your baby questions during a conversation, and start to establish a narrative flow. For example, show them a toy, like their favorite rattle or pacifier. Ask them, "do you want your rattle?" and wait for them to respond positively. Wait until they vocalize their want in some manner, then hand them the rattle.
- Reading is also important; at this point, you should read aloud from books to your child daily. This helps expose them to a much larger set of words, and if the books have pictures, it helps them form associations between those words and their meanings.

Month 6-12

In the later part of the first year, your baby may begin to say the beginnings or endings of words, and it's even possible they will say their first complete word. You should be encouraging this at every step of the way by doing things like:

- Naming everything that they point to or come in contact with. If your child is about to get in the car, say, "we are getting in the car." If your baby is pointing to their food, tell them the name or the utensils you use to feed them.

- Try to be as positive as possible when talking with your baby. If they are fussing, you don't want to say, "stop doing that" you want to say, "it's time to sit still." You can also help them express their feelings by saying them out loud. For example, if they seem giddy or happy, you can say, "whose happy?" and smile back at them.

- Be careful what words you say at this point, as your baby will begin to imitate them fully. This is why curse words should be kept to a minimum (though this becomes more important later on as your child develops their speech abilities fully.) I made the mistake of exclaiming loudly once when I stubbed my toe, and one of our children made that their favorite word for the next month.

Your Relationship With Your Baby is Stronger, But What About With Your Partner?

Bonding with your baby is vital to providing them with the feelings of comfort they need to grow. But the early stages of childhood can be a very straining time for you and your partner, with many parents allowing their romantic relationship to fall by the wayside. In our next chapter, we'll talk about the common challenges and changes that may occur in your relationship and the different ways to solve these new problems.

Dad Hacks From Chapter 6

Mental Health Hack #1: **Mirroring is Key.** Imitation is the sincerest form of flattery, and your baby will be copying your every move. Make sure to return the favor and help reinforce associations between movements and words.

Mental Health Hack #2: **Skin to Skin Contact Helps Bonding.** As one of the strongest tools in your bond-building strategy, skin to skin contact can quickly create a long-lasting emotional connection between you and your baby. Not only that, but it can also relieve stress, lower your baby's heart rate, and help bring their breathing under control.

Mental Health Hack #3: **Don't Overstimulate.** While you want to show your baby a wide variety of photos and help them understand the world around them, it's important not to overstimulate. If your baby begins to get fussy or cry while you teach, take a break to soothe them. A couple of shushes, gentle singing, and a back rub can bring your baby back to calm so they can get back to learning efficiently.

Mental Health Hack #4: **Help Your Baby Finish Words.** As your baby's language centers develop, they will start to vocalize noises that almost sound like full words. Help them finish these words, sounding out each syllable so they can begin to form those associations in their brains.

Mental Health Hack #5: **Identify Everything Around You.** Especially important in the latter half of the first year, you'll want to teach your baby the name of every object, person, and place they interact with. If you make them a mini-Italian dinner, make sure to say, "this is spaghetti." If your sister comes over to visit, let them know, "this is your auntie." These behaviors will make it that much easier once they start to speak and help them understand not only the names of things but the meaning behind those names.

Chapter 7

How to Keep Your Relationship Going Strong, Even After Having a Baby

While having a baby can be one of life's most beautiful and rewarding experiences, it is also difficult, stressful, and exhausting. I'm ashamed to admit it, but my partner and I had our fair share of fights during the first year, often about nothing. I remember waking up late at night, thinking there was an emergency with the baby. Instead, I was confronted with an empty jar of peanut butter, my partner shaking it and whisper-yelling in an accusatory tone. "You ate every last BITE!" she said through gritted teeth, knowing she couldn't wake the baby. In my half-asleep daze, I started laughing; thankfully, so did she. But it goes to show you how stressful sleepless nights can get and how even the silliest thing can set one of you off.

It's strange to go from the two-person unit of a couple to a complete family, and the adjustment period isn't easy. You spend your whole life forming this idea of yourself in your head; then you tack on more years forging a relationship with someone. Now, suddenly, there is this tiny little person who pops into your life. It's a beautiful thing and one of the most significant events you can experience in your life, but it also dumps a myriad of new issues onto your plate. Fortunately, all obstacles can be overcome, and many couples find that they are much stronger for the struggle once they get through to the other side. Let's look at a few relationship changes you can expect after your first baby is born and how to deal with them.

Issue #1: Restructuring Your Lives

Babies are vulnerable and heavily dependent beings, requiring constant attention and care during the first months (and years) of their life. Before your infant is born, even during the pregnancy months, you and your partner will still have a lot of agency as individuals. You may go out, see friends, go on trips, sleep without disruption, and enjoy the freedom that comes without the responsibility of children. Once your kid is born, however, that will shift dramatically. Even if you think you are prepared, this significant change can still do a number on your romantic relationship.

Remember that weekly night out for dinner? You can kiss that goodbye (for a bit.) How about going on a run as a couple or sitting down to cuddle up for a movie? Sayonara. Your baby will need help with feeding, napping, diaper changes and will basically need to be monitored almost every second during the day. This loss of identity can be tough, and it's natural for couples to fight a bit as they feel the weight of that responsibility. My spouse's first stressful tug came with our weekly "old movie" night. We cherished that time, sitting down and picking some ancient black and white film to put on in the background as we inhaled popcorn. But something about those movies just stressed our first child, and we had to do away with the ritual for a while. Become comfortable with sacrifice, and realize that eventually, you'll be able to do most of these activities again.

Issue #2: Sleepless Nights and Weary Days

Sleep deprivation is a wild beast, a monster that, left unchecked, will tear at your sanity and the love you feel for your partner. Unfortunately, some level of sleeplessness is unavoidable during early parenthood. Make sure to look out for the signs of serious sleep deprivation, which include:

- Difficulty Thinking Clearly
- Bad Short-Term Memory
- Poor Decision making
- Lack of Energy
- Reduced Attention Span
- Severe Mood Swings

Sleep deprivation can also fill you with anxiety and make you irritable, something I struggled with. I'm someone who really can't survive without a solid 8 hours, so when I was averaging between 4 and none at all, I was indeed not my best self. Luckily, my spouse is genuinely kind and understanding (as long as you don't eat all of her peanut butter) and puts up with both the baby's temper tantrums and mine.

Issue #3: Feeling Frustrated and Helpless

I won't lie to you: the weight of having a living, breathing person depend on you for their protection and safety is terrifying. Even with all the advice and parenting books in the world, no one can truly prepare you for what it means to be responsible for someone else's life. It's understandable for you and your partner to feel helpless and frustrated with the overwhelming needs of a newborn. There will be times when the baby won't stop crying, can't get to sleep, or won't eat, and it may cause strife in your relationship.

As new problems crop up, remember that you are a team. Give each other breaks, try to research new issues as much as possible, and comfort one another. You may feel upset or sad now and then, especially as you come to understand just how much your baby will need from you. But over time, I promise, it will get easier.

Issue #4: Focusing All of Your Attention on the Baby

Yes, your baby should be the #1 priority in your life after they are born (and probably for the rest of your life as well.) But that doesn't mean that every single scrap and ounce of your attention should go towards your infant. Neglecting to acknowledge and tend to your spouse's needs can devastate your relationship. There will already be a lot of stressors, including the lack of sleep, increasing costs due to childcare, and the loss of free time. Amongst this, it's essential to try your best to remember that your partner is still your partner, and you need to stay connected with them.

If possible, call a family member or friend to see if they can watch the baby for a few hours—just enough time to get some lunch or dinner and get some alone time with your significant other. Remind them how beautiful they are and how much you care about them, and discuss future plans for trips and vacations. The first stages of parenthood can be challenging, and it may feel like it'll be overwhelming forever. Plan for the future and strengthen your relationship any time you can.

Issue #5: Communication Becomes Strained

Communication is vital when it comes to healthy relationships, and a massive life event will understandably shake up your ability to communicate with one another. What used to be sharing thoughts and feelings, regaling each other with stories about your day, and trading cute little inside jokes has become more akin to the communication of ants. When ants talk to each other, they basically just barf up chemicals that send very clear messages. One ant will barf to the other, "food that way", and the other ant will throw up ", okay." While this is great for helping a fellow insect find the picnic, it just doesn't work for human communication.

Just like ants, your conversation may become very one-note and transactional. "The baby is crying", "it's time to change their diaper", and "the baby is hungry"; all of these are examples of the clipped sentences you'll be exchanging in those first few months. As patience runs thin and responsibilities stack, discussions will become demands. Make sure to watch how you talk to your partner and try to make these demands more like requests.

Issue #6: Spontaneity Goes Out the Window

Before the baby, I remember one weekend I came home, and my partner presented me with a plane ticket. "We're going to the coast," she said, her eyes bright and sparkling with excitement. I was taken aback at first, unsure if she was joking, but as she pointed to an open suitcase, I too lit up with excitement. I still look at pictures of that weekend trip, cherishing the memories of sunsets, margaritas, and the sand beneath our feet. Unfortunately, spontaneous trips like this will likely evaporate as the baby arrives.

After your child is born, everything will need to be planned well in advance. Gone are the days of asking, "hey, want to go out for dinner tonight?" as that would require finding a babysitter, getting together a baby bag, and worrying all night about your child. This doesn't mean that you won't have fun, but it will be different. That doesn't mean you can't find ways to surprise your partner, and you should still try to find childcare and go out every once in a while. Just prepare yourself to say goodbye to the gallivanting that you may have once enjoyed as you transition into the responsibility of parenthood.

Issue #7: Your Partner May Suffer from Postpartum Depression

It's very possible that your significant other will experience some form of postpartum depression after birth; dads can get it too! You'll want to watch for the signs of postpartum depression, which include:

- *Lack of Motivation:* One of the early symptoms of postpartum depression is a lack of energy and motivation. If you notice your partner isn't showering, feeding themselves, or generally avoiding self-care, you'll want to talk to them about their feelings. This lack of motivation also extends to tasks relating to your baby. Mothers suffering from PPD may forget to feed or watch their children and will struggle to bond properly.
- *Avoidance:* Another symptom is avoidance of friends and family. If you see your partner ignoring calls, turning friends away at the door, or sequestering themselves when family

173

comes over to see the baby, take these as major red flags. The cause of this avoidance is usually the fear or anxiety that they aren't a good parent, even though these thoughts are almost always unfounded.

- *Mood Swings:* Anger, sadness, anxiety, panic attacks: all of these can accompany postpartum depression. If you see your partner switching through emotions at a fast pace, struggling to sleep at night, or speaking about baby-related fears, check in with them.
- *Thoughts of Harm or Suicide:* This is a more advanced symptom and one of the most worrying. PPD sufferers can begin to have dark thoughts of suicide and, in some cases, even attempt to end their life. They can also have intrusive thoughts about harming the baby, which may be voiced jokingly at first. Recognize this sign for its severity and contact a medical professional immediately.

Don't hesitate to contact a doctor if you believe you or your partner is dealing with postpartum depression. They can help you with treatments to get you through this challenging time; the sooner you seek treatment, the better!

Issue #8: It'll Feel Like You Almost Never Have Sex

It can be a sensitive subject for some, but the issue of sex after having a baby is pretty significant. It's not easy to get in the mood with baby vomit on your shirt and the very unsexy scent of dirty diapers in the air. Even after the four to six weeks of abstinence doctors recommend after birth, you and your partner may have very little interest in sex. You'll start to feel less like lovers and more like roommates who have agreed to take care of a baby.

It's crucial to kindle that intimacy whenever you can. Sex is vital to a healthy romantic relationship and can help boost the confidence of both parties. Not only that, but it's a huge stress reliever, something you'll need during the challenging months following birth.

5 Tips to Keeping Your Relationship Strong Post-Baby

1. See Things from Your Partner's Perspective

Amidst a crisis or in the middle of an argument, it can be hard to approach your spouse from a place of empathy. Tasks get forgotten, things get overlooked, and disagreements get heated. It's important to remember that this is hard on both of you before the voices get raised and the accusations start flying. Sure, a mom's and dad's experiences are different, but at the end of the day, you are in this together. Acknowledge what the other person is going through and try not to "keep score." It's not about who did what on any particular day, but the long game of parenting.

2. Schedule a Weekly Check-in

A good way to get ahead of problems and stay tuned in to how your partner is feeling is with weekly check-ins. My partner and I enacted this practice after a particularly painful week ending a terrible (and utterly useless) fight. I missed a few diapers, she woke the baby up from a nap, and several more minor gaffs culminated in us deciding we needed to make a change. So, we started sequestering our complaints into one weekly session on Sunday; that way, we didn't let our disagreements get in the way of caring for our baby. By the time Sunday rolled around, a lot of the heat of those angry moments had cooled, and we could talk about things more reasonably.

3. Avoid Criticism and Talk Efficiently

A key to effective communication is to avoid criticism whenever possible. Accusing someone of making a mistake, especially when stressed out, will automatically make them defensive. Be intentional with your statements and get right to the problem. Instead of "Can you please give the baby a bath for once?" say, "Honey, I'm so tired I can barely stand. Would you mind bathing the baby tonight?" Approach issues with a bit of tact, and you'll be surprised at how willing your significant other will be to help out.

4. Make Time For Each other

While there won't be time for big romantic getaways in the near future, making time for one another is about the little moments. Hold your partner's hand, tell them how much they mean to you, and spark a conversation about non-baby-related subjects. Remind your significant other that they have their own identity and stay intimate in any way you can. This also means bringing up things you miss, or need, as a partner. That could be a hug, some words of affirmation, or even that it's been a long time since you were physically intimate.

5. "Parent" Each Other

In the same way, you think and care about your infant; you have to care for one another. No, that doesn't mean you'll have to pick up your partner and burp them but instead, give your significant other the same breaks you would give your baby. When your infant starts to get frustrated, I doubt your reaction is to tell them angrily to calm down. Give your partner the benefit of the doubt and try your best to approach them with compassion during this stressful time.

How to Rekindle Your Sex Life After Childbirth

Having a physical connection is important, but passion can understandably slip from your relationship shortly after a baby is born. For several weeks after birth, abstaining from sex is an absolute necessity. Most doctors recommend women avoid sexual activity for four to six weeks, as they need time to heal. There is usually a postpartum check at this point where a doctor will give the go-ahead; even then, some couples find they aren't quite ready to get intimate.

My partner and I struggled with this for some time after baby #1. They didn't feel sexy after the pregnancy, and I didn't feel the urge due to lack of sleep exhaustion; the desire to get intimate wasn't there. I thought this wouldn't be a big deal at first, but then I felt a distance growing between us. Realizing a problem was brewing, I started researching ways to get that passion burning again. Here are a few ways I found to help relight the fire of love and possibly help you start making baby number 2!

Compassion Creates Passion

Sex is a two-way street, and it helps to be compassionate regarding your partner's physical needs. Women often feel overwhelmed after a baby is born and are likely to judge their spouses for their sexual urges. Men, on the other hand, feel rejected and undesired. As these two forces meet and intimacy continues to fade, your relationship can fall into turmoil.

The key is to tap into that compassion and ask your partner about their sexual feelings. Be empathetic, listen to their side of the story, and share your own. By opening up communication and doing your best to understand what they are going through, you can bring back those feelings of closeness that inspired you to be intimate in the first place.

Small Gestures Make Big Impacts

I'm guilty of that old trope, the "grand romantic gesture." I made a bit of a gaff after our second child, in which I organized some time away only a few months after they were born. I was frustrated when my partner wasn't excited to go after booking hotels and finding childcare. But she explained her feelings, that she wasn't ready to be away from the baby, and I realized I was being a bit selfish. I should have talked with her first, instead of trying to surprise her with an impromptu vacation.

Small gestures are a much better and more manageable way to show affection for your partner. An "I love you text" when you are apart, a kiss at the start of the day, a home-cooked meal or their favorite takeout. It may not sound sexy, but getting someone food from their favorite Chinese restaurant can be the most romantic thing in the world.

Schedule Intimate Time

What's sexier than breaking out a calendar and saying, "hey, when are you free?" Okay, that doesn't actually sound sexy at all. But with the cramped work schedule, taking care of the baby, and everything else in your lives, scheduling intimacy may be the best solution to a temporary dry spell. Pick a time once a week when you and your partner can have a night to yourselves (after the baby has gone to bed.)

Put the phones away, unplug the television, and spend some time talking, cuddling, and hopefully more. Remind your partner why you find them attractive, and don't be afraid to make the first move. Your significant other is likely just as sexually frustrated as you are. That being said, if they aren't in the mood, there are other ways to be intimate. Simply holding one another, kissing, and talking about anything but the baby can help strengthen your connection.

Get Naked and Give Gifts

It can be hard to remember that you and your partner are sexual creatures when you are constantly clothed in the classic parent's uniform: baggy t-shirt, flat grey sweatpants, and well-worn slippers. Shed those clothes whenever you can, even if you don't plan to have sex. Feeling comfortable with your body and even doing something as simple as walking around naked can ease the stress; not only that, but it's more than likely to lead to something more.

You can also spark intimacy with some sexually suggestive gifts. If you've been with your significant other for a long time, your sex life may have become a bit stagnant. This can aggravate the intimacy struggle that follows birth; the solution is to try new things. Talk with your partner about their fantasies, and surprise them with a gift that fulfills them.

Reclaim Some Space

A baby can sometimes feel like a very territorial and poorly behaved roommate. Suddenly, this tiny tyrant has taken over the whole of your house. They are up late, making noise and constantly present when you are trying to spend time with your partner. Pictures of the baby replace photos of your time together as a couple, everyone asks about your child whenever they see you, and every single event seems to revolve around your infant. It's hard to feel attractive when you've lost your identity as an individual and as a couple. The solution is to reclaim a bit of space!

Now, this doesn't mean deprioritizing your baby. But there are little things you can do to remind your partner and yourself that you are people. Keep some photos of your time as a couple, talk to your partner about fun trips you took before the baby, and try to have a space in the house that is just for you and your significant other. Recapture some ground for yourselves, and you'll be surprised at how quickly the intimacy returns.

Your Baby, Your Relationship, and Your Work Life: How Can You Balance Everything?

Now that we've talked about a few ways to reignite the intimacy in your relationship, let's move to the juggling act of fatherhood. You need to be a parent and a partner, and you'll also likely need to keep working. Keeping all these plates spinning isn't easy but keeping your finances in order is an absolute necessity. In our next chapter, we'll discuss a few ways to keep your work and life balanced, manage your finances, analyze expenses, and save money during the first year of your baby's life.

Dad Hacks From Chapter 7

Relationship Hack #1: You'll Need to Sacrifice a Few Things. Parenthood is all about sacrifice, and you'll have to become comfortable letting certain things go. Your life has changed dramatically, and you'll lose some of your autonomy. Some of it will come back in time, but some won't (and that's okay!)

Relationship Hack #2: Prepare for Sleeplessness. Sleep is incredibly important, but getting the right amount of rest as a new parent is not possible. Watch for the signs of sleep exhaustion, including confusion, lack of energy, and irritability. Do what you can to nap when your partner is watching the baby, and know that your sleep schedule will eventually normalize.

Relationship Hack #3: Watch for the Signs of Postpartum Depression. PPD is incredibly serious, so watch for the signs that your partner may suffer from this illness. These signs include:

- Lack of motivation
- Mood swings
- Avoidance of others
- Thoughts of suicide or harming the baby

If you recognize the symptoms of PPD, contact your doctor immediately.

Relationship Hack #4: Be Patient With Your Partner. Being a new parent is incredibly difficult, and it's understandable to get frustrated when your significant other makes a mistake. Try to see the situation from their shoes and understand you are both tired and stressed out. Patience pays off, and when you give your spouse the benefit of the doubt, they are more likely to return the favor.

Relationship Hack #5: Rekindle Your Sex Life. Don't let the intimacy in your relationship slip away due to the responsibilities of parenthood. Remind your partner that you find them sexually desirable, find time to spend together, and respark the fire of love in your life. It may take a few weeks or months after the baby is born, but once your partner is ready, get back in the bedroom!

Chapter 8

How to Juggle Work and Life as a New Dad

A father isn't just a caretaker and provider, he is also a performer. Like someone spinning plates or juggling flaming bowling pins, a dad needs to understand how to keep everything moving together in (almost) perfect harmony. Once your child is born, you can basically bisect your life into two major parts: time spent at work and time spent at home. Both carry a significant amount of importance: your time at home life will define how much of your energy you can dedicate to being a father and partner, while your time spent at work will determine how well you can provide for your family. Achieving a perfect balance between these two parts isn't possible, but you'll want to get as close as you can. Let's look at a few ways you can balance work and life as a new dad.

5 Ways to Balance Work and Life as a New Dad

1. Set Your Priorities

While arranging your time in both your role as a dad and a worker won't be simple, the process will be easier if you set short and long term priorities. Obviously, you want to spend as much time as possible with your child. At the same time, you need to make sure that your family is supported financially. This will require a bit of compromise in each of your roles.

You'll need to be realistic about what you can accomplish in a day and plan accordingly. If your job frequently requires you to stay late, it may not be possible to agree to extra responsibilities for your child. This is an example from a bit later on in my parenthood journey, I was asked to coach my first child's soccer team. Unfortunately, due to my work duties I had to decline. Instead, I made sure to take time off or leave early on days when there were games and attend as many as possible. Making a compromise like this can show your child you care about them without causing you to lose too much ground at work.

2. Use Your Time as Effectively as Possible

Try to plan out the hours of your day and set aside as much time as possible for your child. This could mean waking up a bit earlier to spend time with the baby before you leave for work or sacrificing drinks with your co-workers to come home and play with your child before bed. You can still have a bit of time to yourself and your friends, but remember tip #1: you have to decide what your priorities are and dedicate the majority of your time to those.

You can also plan ahead and change your behavior to save time with activities like meal prep. Choose a day of the week, like Sunday, and make all of your lunches for the week. This will give you a bigger chunk of time each day to either catch up on work or play with your child. There are also apps and services that can be great time savers. Grocery delivery services can save you hours of wandering through stores, a task that can be all the more difficult with an infant. I can't tell you how many times I've been stuck on a work call with my child in the cart, desperately trying to navigate my conversation while preventing my kid from grabbing food from the shelves. In my experience, it's better to pay a bit more to have the whole shopping ordeal taken care of for you.

3. Discuss Issues with Your Partner

Remember, you aren't in this alone! Talk to your significant other about your work-life concerns, and see what solutions they may have. They will most likely be willing to take on more baby tasks on certain days to ease your stress. For instance, if you have a big meeting coming up the next day, ask your partner if they would be willing to watch the baby so you can prepare. You may feel guilty asking them to do extra work, but if something is important, I'm sure your partner will be understanding.

You can also make plans with your significant other concerning both of your work schedules. With my partner, we had an issue early on balancing child-care and both of our jobs. We were trying to save a bit of money by not using a daycare every day of the work week, but the stress was starting to get overwhelming. We decided it was well worth the extra money, and sacrificed some money we had been saving for a vacation. Even though it was sad to see our Jamaican cruise money go up in smoke, it was a necessary compromise to help that work-life balance become more manageable.

4. Turn off the Tech

Both my partner and I have our own separate technology addictions, each for different reasons. She is a true crime fanatic and constantly listening to podcasts or perusing forums, while I'm always plugged into my fantasy football league. After the baby, we both had to take a step back and realize we were hooked up to our devices for a majority of the day.

Part of the issue with completely cutting myself off from my phone and computer is that sometimes my work needs to contact me after hours. Admittedly, I made myself a bit too available to calls and emails; a lot of the time, it was something that could have easily waited until work hours. So after the baby was born, I let my department know: unless it was of vital importance, I wouldn't be answering messages outside of the office. Surprisingly, they had no problem with this at all! This gave me much more time to spend with my child, and helped me establish boundaries between my work life and my home life.

5. Talk with Your Work about Flexibility

Speaking of work discussions, you will likely have told your supervisors about the baby well before they are born. Part of this discussion should be about your work hours, and trying to create a schedule that allows you to help out at home as much as possible. You'd be surprised how many workplaces will be flexible when it comes to childcare, and there may even be programs your company has set up to assist you.

Working from home is one way to help you save time, and if your job is the type that can be done remotely, talk to your boss about splitting your hours between the office and your home. By working remotely, you can eliminate the time wasted commuting, as well as take small breaks throughout the day to spend time with your child. Working from home can also reduce the financial burden of finding childcare services. Overall, remote work is one of the best ways to get the balance you are looking for when it comes to your job and home life.

Financial Tips for New Dads: How to Get More Out of Your Money

Part of the reason that creating a work-life balance is so difficult is that, no matter how you slice it, having a kid requires a significant amount of money. You want to spend every second with your baby, but at the same time, you have to shoulder the financial burden of food, diapers, toys, and everything else that your child needs. To make this easier, you'll want to make sure your finances are as orderly as possible. Here are a few tips that can make that process much smoother.

Tip #1: Create a Budget

The first step to improving your financial health is to create a budget. Map out your income and expenses, taking special note of whether you are spending your money on "wants" or "needs". When I first put together a budget, I noticed I was spending an *insane* amount of money on coffee each month. I didn't think much of it as I was calculating the amount, saying to myself "plenty of people get a coffee every day, how much could it really be?" After I hit enter on the calculator, I was shocked to see I was spending **over $200** on coffee each and every month. After raising my hands to the sky and cursing my favorite coffee shop, I purchased a nice coffee maker online. Now getting coffee is a very rare treat, and I have more money for the things that matter.

Tip #2: Take Advantage of Credit Card Benefits

Building credit and using all of the benefits your bank offers is essential to strengthening your finances. If your credit score is low, fixing it should be a priority. Make a list of all of your payments, whether it be for your car, cards, or any loans you have, and ensure you consistently pay them on time. Credit utilization is especially important; if your cards are constantly maxed out, your credit score will drop dramatically. Over time your score will rise, making it easier to get loan approval and lower interest.

You should also look at your credit card benefits. Many cards have cash back or redeemable points that come with making purchases. These points can be used for rewards like food, gas, airline miles, and many other things that can help reduce your expenses. As long as you can pay the cards off, try to put as much of your purchasing as possible onto your credit cards (using your debit card likely won't give you the same benefits as using your credit cards.)

Tip #3: Make Sure You Have an Emergency Fund

Life is unpredictable, and having an emergency fund can give you one of the most valuable things a parent can have: peace of mind. Shortly after our first child was born, I got into a car accident. Thankfully I was the only one in the car, and I wasn't hurt. I wish I could say the same for my Honda! With my vehicle totaled, and my insurance slow to approve my claim, I had to pay for the damages myself so I could keep commuting to work. Luckily, I had my emergency fund; what could have been an incredibly difficult problem was downgraded to only a minor inconvenience.

For your emergency fund to have a sufficient amount of money, make sure it can cover 6 to 12 months of your monthly expenses. This money can come in handy for a number of situations including:

- Vehicle Troubles
- Job Loss
- Medical Emergency
- Unexpected Travel Expenses
- Emergency Home Repairs

Tip #4: Get Life Insurance and Make a Will

It's tough to think about, but one important financial factor is preparing for the worst case scenario. An official will and solid life insurance policy can be massively helpful to your family in the event of your death, helping both your partner and your child through what would already be an overwhelming period of time. If you can try, try to get your life insurance through your employers, as they usually offer the best rates. Shoot for a policy that covers 10 times your annual income, as this would give your family a substantial buffer if you were to suddenly pass away.

As for a will, this will be something you'll want to talk about with your partner. It can be tempting to avoid this as long as possible, as the thought of you or your significant other passing away is devastating. But for legal reasons, neglecting to have a will can make the already arduous process of spousal death that much more complicated. Talk to an estate lawyer in your area about what the best way to draw up a will, as well as decide who will have the power of attorney for both your finances and healthcare. I chose my partner, but it's entirely possible you have someone else in mind. This person will be able to control both your money and your medical care if you are ever unable to do so, like if you are in a coma or any other type of incapacitated state.

Tip #5: Choose Safe Investments

While keeping your money in a savings account may seem safe, it won't do much in the way of growth. Check what retirement contribution plans your employer offers, like a 401k. You'll also want to see what wealth management services your bank offers, as well as plans you can create to start saving for your child's college education. A 529 plan is a good example of this type of savings; with a 529 plan, you can deposit money without paying federal taxes and won't pay penalties when funds are withdrawn for educational purposes. Anyone can contribute to a 529, meaning that relatives and loved ones can put money in as a gift to you or your children.

You'll also want to avoid risky or highly speculative forms of investing, like cryptocurrency or individual stocks. Total market ETFs are okay, but the issue comes in when you place large amounts of money into what is essentially gambling. I remember getting a hot tip from a friend about this smaller cryptocurrency, and regrettably threw a few thousand dollars down. I thought "well if he's right, and this goes up 1000%, my child's education will be fully paid for! I'd be irresponsible not to do it, right?" You can guess how this story ends; let's just say, I'm still saving for future education expenses. Skip the risky bets, and stick to sustainable growth over the long term.

Tip #6: Don't Forget to Have a "Fun" Fund!

Just because you aren't blowing all your paychecks on extravagant getaways or expensive toys doesn't mean you can't have fun every now and then. In the early days after the baby is born, when the stress is building, get together with your partner and talk about a fun future trip. Brainstorm up places you've always wanted to go, look up flight and hotel packages, talk about all the different activities you want to do while you're there, and put the plan down on paper. Obviously this won't take place further down the road, but you can even talk about whether you'd be comfortable having close relatives watch the baby for the duration of the trip. This can be incredibly helpful to alleviate that "cooped up" feeling that often accompanies early parenthood.

Once the plan is set, start saving. During those planning stages make sure to draft up the rough costs this type of trip would incur, including travel expenses, food, lodging, and childcare if that applies. You can create a savings account specifically for the trip (labeling it something like "Las Vegas 2025" or whatever name would apply) and make regular deposits. This also gives you and your partner something to look forward to, and a discussion topic that does not involve your child.

How Can I Save Money on My Baby's Necessities?

Having a baby is expensive, and feeling that financial strain can make an already stressful situation that much worse. Here are a few ways you can save money during the first year of your baby's life.

- *Feeding:* If possible, talk to your partner about primarily breastfeeding as opposed to formula feeding, as this can drastically reduce food costs. Look into purchasing a decent breast pump along with breast milk storage bottles and bags. This is what we did with our second child, and by the end of the first year we had saved almost $1000.
- *Diapers:* I'm personally guilty of using disposable diapers, so I completely understand not having the time or energy to go the more affordable route. But if you can, cloth diapers are far easier on the wallet and way better for the environment. Cloth diapers are reusable, and there are even services that will deliver them to your home and give you better prices if you buy in bulk.
- *Baby Toys:* As parents, we all want to spoil our children with all the toys they could want. The fact of the matter is, infants really don't need much in that first year. Stick with a few baby-safe toys, mostly ones that they can chew on without any risk of choking. Your baby isn't going to get bored of one toy and want another, because frankly, they aren't forming those types of memories yet.
- *Baby Clothes:* Baby's grow quickly, and while it may look cute to have them decked out in neat outfits for every stage of their growth, it just isn't financially sound. Talk to your friends who have also had children, as they may have some

secondhand baby clothes you can use. If you do buy clothes, try to shop for the deals and see what you can get for more affordable prices. That big price tag onesie may look cute on the rack, but once it's covered in stains, you'll probably regret the money you spent.

Baby Care Tasks Worksheet

To help you and your partner allocate your time more efficiently, try to track how many hours you spend completing various household and childcare related tasks each week. I've placed a sample chart below. You may want to modify the chart with your own tasks, but this is a good framework to help you get started.

Task	Monday	Tuesday	Wednesda	Thursday	Friday	Saturday	Sunday
Baby Bath Time							
Baby Play Time							
Laundry							
Getting Baby Ready for Sleep							
Cooking							
Washing Dishes							
Paying Bills							
Vehicle Maintenance							
Shopping for Food							
Taking Care of Pets							
Mowing/Gardening							
Going to Work							
Cleaning the House							

Taking the Baby Outdoors								
School work (if applicable)								
Talking on the Phone (for work or other purposes)								
Changing Diapers								
Cleaning Up Baby-Related Messes								

Babies May Take a Lot of Time and Money, But It's Always Worth It

Balancing both your time and finances may be difficult, but once you find that sweet spot, you'll start to notice everything gets a bit easier. Believe me, it's possible to succeed at work AND make sure your baby feels loved, but it may take a bit for you to master your juggling act. Now, we've covered a lot of topics in this book, and it's understandable if there are certain sections you want to review. In the conclusion that follows, we'll look back at the subjects we've talked about and give a brief overview for each.

Dad Hacks From Chapter 8

Balance Hack #1: Prioritize What's Important. It's a tough pill to swallow, but the fact is there just isn't time for everything. Make a list of all of your responsibilities, and try to rank them based on importance. Being a dad will come first most of the time, this is a give-in; that being said, maintaining your status at work is also vital to your family's financial health. Learn to prioritize the most essential activities, and become comfortable with compromise.

Balance Hack #2: Time Management is Essential. There are only so many hours in the day, but you'd be surprised how much time we waste. Between our phones, TV, drinks after work, and every other leisurely activity, we rarely use each day to its full potential. Breakdown how you use your time, eliminating unavoidable activities like work at sleep. Look at the hours you have left and try to fill them with as much productivity as possible (making sure to give yourself a small chunk each day for "me-time").

Balance Hack #3: Prepare for the Unexpected. Parenthood is a lot like improve, and you'll need to roll with the punches when it comes to dealing with the challenges that get thrown your way. Part of this is thinking about the more unfortunate turns life can take, like…well, death. Creating a will and getting a life insurance policy, while a bit of a bummer, can give you valuable peace of mind as you raise your children. Knowing your significant other and children will be safe in the case of your passing can allow you to focus on the present, and be the best dad you possibly can.

Balance Hack #4: **Create a Budget.** Budgeting is a life skill that can help anyone, parent or not. Calculating your income and tallying up your expenses can help you keep a healthy financial flow, as well as highlight any extraneous spending you may have. I was shocked when I laid out my budget on how much I was spending on things like eating out at restaurants and getting coffee every day. Cooking at home and making my own coffee saved me hundreds of dollars every month, which allowed me to make more significant contributions to my child's college fund.

Balance Hack #5: **Don't Forget the Fun.** While it is important to work hard and give your all when it comes to being a father, you still need to schedule in some time for yourself. Neglecting to do so can lead to increased stress, which will start to hamper your performance both in the workplace and at home. Make sure to invest time in a hobby, and try your best to have a night out with friends every once and a while. Your spouse will also need some "me" time, so talk with each other about how you can adjust your schedules to make this happen.

Conclusion

Despite the trials and tribulations of parenthood, nothing can bring you more joy in this life than having a baby. Yes, it comes with responsibilities, but you'll be amazed what you can accomplish when you have the love of a family behind you. No one is a perfect dad, even those of us that have been fathers for many years. But with genuine care, attention, and a willingness to stick out even the toughest monuments, you can give your child the foundation they need to grow up happy, confident, and ready for life's challenges. Remember, many things in life are challenging in the beginning; few things worth fighting for are easy. But just like gold hidden deep beneath the earth, your baby is a treasure. The first 12 months can be tough, but with the information I've compiled here, and your own strong will, I know you will be able to get through it.

To help you review the information we've covered in this book, let's go chapter by chapter and highlight the most important bits of information.

Chapter 1: What to Expect and What to Do When Your Baby is Born

In Chapter 1 we discussed how to prep your home for the baby's arrival and what you can expect in the first 24 hours after you return from the hospital. This included ways to babyproof your home, like taking care of any sharp corners, dangerous cords, or potentially consumable chemicals. For the first 24 hours, we looked at what should be done at the hospital (like expecting the placenta and helping your spouse get skin-to-skin contact with the baby) along with the first feedings and all tests that will take place right after birth.

Chapter 2: Basic Care for Your Baby

Chapter 2 covered the basic ways to take care of your baby, including:

- *Changing Diapers:* As a dad, you'll be changing your fair share of diapers, so it's best to be prepared. The chapter talks about how to pack and bring a diaper bag, the proper way to change a diaper, and all the associated materials you'll need to do a diaper change.
- *Bathing the Baby:* We also discussed the right way to bathe a baby and how frequently your baby needs a bath. The chapter also covers how full a bath should be, what temperature the water should reach, and what types of soaps to use when washing your baby.
- *How to Deal With Crying:* Chapter 2 talks about the reasons that babies cry, and when crying is normal or due to an illness (like colic). We also discussed the danger of shaken baby syndrome, and the proper ways to help your child when they are crying.

The chapter concluded by discussing SIDS, including the causes, risk factors, and how to prevent this syndrome from occurring.

Chapter 3: How to Feed Your Baby the Right Way

In Chapter 3 we covered the right ways to feed your baby, including how to establish a feeding schedule. Your baby may be getting its nutrients from a few sources, including breastfeeding or bottle feeding with formula. The chapter then goes into introducing solids at around the four month mark and how to properly store these foods. The chapter closes on keeping your baby hydrated, talking about when it's okay to give your baby water and when they can have other beverages like juice.

Chapter 4: How to Help Your Baby Sleep

Chapter 4 was all about making sure your baby gets the right amount of sleep to facilitate healthy brain development and avoid cognition issues later in life. The chapter begins by discussing infant sleeping patterns in different stages, including:

- 0-3 months
- 3-6 months
- 6-12 months

We also covered the signs that your baby isn't getting enough sleep, including that they are having trouble getting settled, rubbing their eyes, fussing, and moving around uneasily. We also talked about some healthy sleep tips, like making sure your baby gets natural sunlight in the morning, establishing a bedtime routine, and the best way to rock your baby to sleep. The chapter closes on some common sleep problems you'll encounter during the first 12 months of your baby's life and how you can solve them.

Chapter 5: How to Teach Your Baby to Develop Self-Regulation

In Chapter 5 we went over the temperament of infants, and how learning self-control and self-regulation early on can help your baby as they develop into their adolescence. To avoid undue stress, a baby needs to learn to self-soothe, but the skill will grow slowly. The chapter covers the self-regulation abilities of infants over the first 12 months of their lives, primarily in months 0-3, 3-6, and 6-12. Each section covers the different behaviour's your baby will exhibit, and some tips on how you can help create the right environment for them to self-soothe. The chapter closes on some ways you can increase self-control and self-confidence in your child, as well as the best ways to tune-in to their temperament.

Chapter 6: How to Help Your Baby Develop Their Emotional and Mental Health

Following the chapter on self-regulation, we covered the further development of your baby's mental and emotional health. Chapter 6 starts on some tips for each developmental stage, including:

- *Month 0-3:* Engaging their senses, using baby talk, soothing, and stimulating
- *Month 3-6:* Showing your baby photos, mirroring their sounds, and encouraging them to interact with objects
- *Month 6-12:* Allowing your baby to explore the house, speaking full words to them, and connecting sounds with gestures

The chapter then went on to talk about ways to bond with your baby. These tips include smiling/talking with your baby, making funny faces, singing, getting skin-to-skin contact, and having one-on-one time. The chapter ends on a breakdown of each stage and the best ways to bond with your baby during each.

Chapter 7: How to Keep Your Relationship Going Strong, Even After Having a Baby

In Chapter 7 we talked about how having a baby can affect your relationships, and the different issues that can cause strife right after the birth of your child. Some of these issues included:

- Needing to restructure your lives
- Lack of sleep and the associated problems that creates
- The feelings of frustration or hopelessness of early parenthood
- Focusing all of your attention on your baby and none on your partner
- The strain a baby can put on communication
- The lack of spontaneity once you have a child
- The possibility of postpartum depression
- The lack of sex during the first year of parenthood

The chapter then covered five tips to helping your relationship say strong post baby:

1. See Things from Your Partner's Perspective
2. Schedule a Weekly Check-in
3. Avoid Criticism and Talk Efficiently
4. Make Time For Each other
5. "Parent" Each Other

The chapter closed on some ways to rekindle your sex life after childbirth, like creating passion, making small gestures, scheduling intimate time, getting naked, and reclaiming some space for you and your significant other.

Chapter 8: How to Juggle Work and Life as a New Dad

The final chapter covered ways to balance your work life and home life as a new father. Chapter 8 begins with five balancing tips, including:

1. Set Your Priorities
2. Use Your Time as Effectively as Possible
3. Discuss Issues with Your Partner
4. Turn off the Tech (take a break from devices)
5. Talk with Your Work about Flexibility

The chapter then delved into some financial tips for new dads and how to get more out of your money. These tips included:

1. Create a Budget
2. Take Advantage of Credit Card Benefits
3. Create an Emergency Fund
4. Get Life Insurance and Make a Will
5. Make Sure You Choose Safe Investments
6. Create a "Fun" Fund (for vacations, etc)

The chapter closes on how to save money on baby necessities, like food, diapers, toys, and clothes. I also included a baby care tasks worksheet, so you and your partner can see if you are splitting house and baby chores evenly.

What I Want You To Take Away

Every father starts as a novice, and with this book, I hope to impart as much knowledge as possible to make the journey a bit easier. By paying attention to the little things, strengthening your partnership with your spouse, and remembering to tend to your baby's emotional needs, you can set your family up for a bright and prosperous future.

If you enjoyed this book, it would mean the world to me if you left a review on Amazon. I believe the work I've put into these chapters can help new fathers reduce some of the stress of early parenthood and learn some tips that can make the first 12 months a more manageable mountain to summit. While the first year may seem arduous, I promise you will look back one day and miss when your child was this small. Take pictures, videos, make scrapbooks, do anything you can to crystallize these memories for the future. That's one of the most important tips I can give you: cherish every moment. Life is short, and your children will only be babies once. Yes, it will get tough. But I promise you, every sleepless night, every argument with your partner, every dirty diaper, is 100% worth it in the end.

I would be glad to hear your feedback about this book, both from the perspective of how it applied to your experience and what you learned from your real-life experience that could have been included here. Feel free to email me at: http://williamhardingauthor.com/.

If you think the book was helpful and that it is worthy of a nice review, please leave one on Amazon or your venue of choice. This will help dads that you don't even know to prepare for this phase of their life and look forward to enjoying their future.

Thanks for reading this work. I look forward to creating more in the future.

Reviews

As an independent author with a small marketing budget, reviews are my livelihood on this platform. If you enjoyed this book, I'd really appreciate it if you left your honest feedback. I love hearing from my readers, and I personally read every single review.

Join the Dads Club Community

DAD's Club: Support Group For Dads | Facebook

References

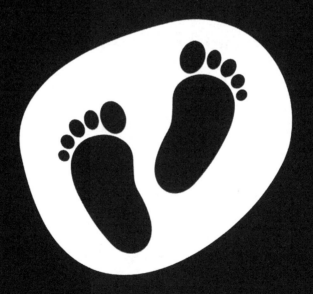

FIRST TIME DAD KEEPSAKE MEMOIR,
PROMPTS AND TO-DOS FOR PREGNANCY TO HELP YOU
FEEL PREPARED FOR YOUR NEW-BORN

NEW DAD
JOURNAL

WILLIAM HARDING

NEW DAD JOURNAL

First Time Dad Keepsake Memoir,
Prompts and To-Dos for Pregnancy
to Help You Feel Prepared
for Your New-Born

William Harding

This Journal belongs to

....

INTRODUCTION

Hi, my name is William Harding, thanks for grabbing a copy of my first-time dad's Journal. Often, I find most readers just read a book and don't take any action or follow up on any key takeaways. I designed this with you in mind every step of the way. I have been in your shoes, and I know reading without implementing actions often leads to no action being followed through.

Take control and plan your way through each step of the journey, once you can master this you can truly enjoy the journey of fatherhood knowing you have intentionally set up a plan.

Your partner will feel better supported and these are all the necessary tasks to make sure your journey is smooth therefore just be prepared.

Fill-in-the-blank space which is provided for your thoughts in answer to those questions. Plan your answers to the questions and work with your partner for a team effort.

The key is to take positive action and to start thinking about the answers. Write down your first thoughts. Even if you know your first thought will not be your final answer. There is no such thing as a wrong answer.

You can work through different sections if you are ahead of some planning or decide to start in a different area, its designed for you to use as you wish.

Additional space is provided so you can record your further thoughts and ideas. The more you consider the questions and your answers, the clearer your thinking will become. It is worth reviewing the questions and prior answers from scratch every day. Over a month your answers will evolve and lead you to have all the right answers. Let's start the planning and reflection, I hope you enjoy this, and it creates a sense of peace of mind that your journey is in order, and you can leave behind a treasure of reflected thoughts.

"When my father didn't have my hand, he had my back."

– Linda Poindexter

THE 1ST TRIMESTER

WEEKS 0 - 14

WHATS HAPPENING WITH BABY

What Is Happening with the Baby? In the first weeks of pregnancy, the baby is just starting to form, and by the end of the first month is still about the size of a grain of rice. While more features begin to emerge over the coming weeks, they are hardly recognizable. Even by the end of the second month, if you were to see the fetus, it would look more like some sort of prehistoric animal (or alien) than anything human. Four weeks more into the maturing miracle, the fetus is only about an inch long. It has managed to nurture more changes in your partner's physiology than its own.

Almost like the magic of a lump of clay becoming a beautiful creation in the hands of an artisan, the fetus looks far more human by the end of the trimester. The baby is still tiny and quite fragile. Even at that small size, the baby is essentially fully formed, although in miniature. The little fingers and toes begin to grow nails, and small movements begin in the extremities and jaw. While there is still not much size and mass, it is about three inches long and right about an ounce. For dads, let's say about the size of a strangely shaped baseball—the risk of any complications that have not already been identified drops significantly. Because the 14th week is recognized with the decrease in risk, it is often the milestone where couples choose to reveal the little miracle.

However, do not ignore that complications can still arise if you let your guard down. There is still no room for working with hazardous chemicals and cleaning products. Eating safely and paying attention to everything the mother encounters is critical to the fetus' further development.

WHATS HAPPENING WITH YOUR PARTNER

The sudden and grotesque emergence of hormones in the pregnant mother is nothing short of volcanic and chaotic. Even women who have proven throughout a relationship to be relatively stable troopers during the trials and tribulations of menstrual cycles may suddenly find their bane in the surge of blossoming motherhood. Picking a daisy may cause uncontrollable weeping. Swooning from nausea may lead to the inability to get out of bed with only the comfort of a vomit bowl and Saltines in close reach. Smells like the cologne she bought you for Christmas may lead to hissing reminders to take a shower. Mind you, she picked the scent, and she now rages at it in a passion.

There will be no respite from the primordial response, and she can't take a pill to fix it without endangering the whole reason for the presence of the onslaught. The father might well be tempted to consider a vacation to a foreign land just for a short 14 weeks or so, but the truth is that this is when you may be needed the most. Getting screamed at in the birthing room is nothing compared to the potential tempest that threatens to cleave oceans in two and scatter the broken hulls of boats on the rocks. But the waves of turmoil can ease just as quickly to sad moments and calm. Changes in blood flow cause discomfort in the form of constipation and swelling of the breasts. It may be best to designate a particular bathroom off-limits to anyone but the mother if you have the luxury of more than one. The growing frequency of peeing increases in concert with nausea, and the whole makes having a b-line to the facilities all but essential.

What I described here is the worst-case scenario. Some women go through the first 14 weeks with barely any symptoms at all. Your spouse is experiencing a chemical cocktail as she has never had before. Just as patients respond differently to various medications, the result comes down to an individual's experience with their change. You might experience every bit of the horror, or barely any at all.

IM GOING TO BE A DAD!

Date I Found Out ....

My Reaction

....
....
....
....

How I Revealed To My Spouse

....
....
....
....

Immediate Family Reaction

....
....
....

How Did We Tell Our Loved Ones

....
....
....
....

APPOINTMENT LOG

Date

Doctor's Name

Weight

Blood Pressure

To Do

Not To Do

Important Notes

Dear Baby,

MONTHLY JOURNAL

5 MINUTE JOURNALING

TOP 3 THINGS ABOUT THIS MONTH

○

○

○

WHAT INSPIRED YOU THE MOST THIS MONTH?

WHAT EMOTIONS HAVE YOU FELT TODAY?

HOW WOULD YOU RATE THE MONTH?

☆ ☆ ☆ ☆ ☆

3 THINGS I WISH FOR TOMORROW

○

○

○

MONTHLY CHECK IN

TODAY I AM FEELING...

TODAY I AM GOING TO...

TODAY I AM LOOKING FORWARD TO...

MY AFFIRMATION TODAY

WEEK 1

Date ....   **Baby Size** ....

Weight ....   **Belly Measurement** ....

3 Things that happened this week

My childhood memory

Excited About

Challenges

Thoughts and Feelings

WEEK 2

Date .... **Baby Size** ....

Weight .... **Belly Measurement** ....

3 Things that happened this week

My childhood memory

Excited About

Challenges

Thoughts and Feelings

WEEK 3

Date .... **Baby Size** ....

Weight .... **Belly Measurement** ....

3 Things that happened this week

My childhood memory

Excited About

Challenges

Thoughts and Feelings

WEEK 4

Date ....   **Baby Size** ....

Weight ....   **Belly Measurement** ....

3 Things that happened this week   My childhood memory

Excited About   Challenges

Thoughts and Feelings

WEEK 5

Date .... **Baby Size** ....

Weight .... **Belly Measurement** ....

3 Things that happened this week

My childhood memory

Excited About

Challenges

Thoughts and Feelings

WEEK 6

Date .... **Baby Size** ....

Weight .... **Belly Measurement** ....

3 Things that happened this week

My childhood memory

Excited About

Challenges

Thoughts and Feelings

WEEK 7

Date .... **Baby Size** ....

Weight .... **Belly Measurement** ....

3 Things that happened this week

My childhood memory

Excited About

Challenges

Thoughts and Feelings

WEEK 8

Date .... **Baby Size** ....

Weight .... **Belly Measurement** ....

3 Things that happened this week

My childhood memory

Excited About

Challenges

Thoughts and Feelings

WEEK 9

Date .... **Baby Size** ....

Weight .... **Belly Measurement** ....

3 Things that happened this week

My childhood memory

Excited About

Challenges

Thoughts and Feelings

WEEK 10

Date .... **Baby Size** ....

Weight .... **Belly Measurement** ....

3 Things that happened this week

My childhood memory

Excited About

Challenges

Thoughts and Feelings

WEEK 11

Date ....   **Baby Size** ....

Weight ....   **Belly Measurement** ....

3 Things that happened this week   My childhood memory

Excited About   Challenges

Thoughts and Feelings

WEEK 12

Date ....   **Baby Size** ....

Weight ....   **Belly Measurement** ....

3 Things that happened this week   My childhood memory

Excited About   Challenges

Thoughts and Feelings

WEEK 13

Date _____ **Baby Size** _____

Weight _____ **Belly Measurement** _____

3 Things that happened this week

My childhood memory

Excited About

Challenges

Thoughts and Feelings

WEEK 14

Date _____ **Baby Size** _____

Weight _____ **Belly Measurement** _____

3 Things that happened this week   My childhood memory

Excited About   Challenges

Thoughts and Feelings

BABY NAME IDEAS

HOWS DAD DOING.............

5 MINUTE JOURNALING

"Of all the titles I've been privileged to have, Dad has always been the best."

-Ken Norton

THE 2ND TRIMESTER

WEEKS 15 TO 27

WHAT IS HAPPENING WITH THE BABY?

The baby has become recognizably human by the 14th week and is only going to start growing more rapidly. Starting at about 4 inches by week 15, the fetus will grow to about half an inch per week, getting up to about 9 inches by the end of the trimester with growth in bodily length accelerating.

During the first month of the trimester, the fetus begins to sexually mature, with males forming a prostate and females developing ovaries and what will mature into their life-long store of eggs of their own. Hair will grow along with a mucus-like substance (vernix caseosa) which helps to protect the skin in the aqueous environment where they are developing.

In the later months, the formation of hair extends to eyebrows, and other fine physical attributes such as taste buds mature. Your budding flower is essentially a miniature human in every way by the end of the trimester and only goes on to advance in these stages of development in the approaching trimester.

The "lump of clay" had made a significant advancement in taking final form. Remain diligent and alert to dangers in the environment. Try and be helpful with your partner's diet, which will continue to morph and flourish. Everything that passes her lips still plays a part in the development of the child.

WHAT IS HAPPENING TO YOUR PARTNER?

Around week 13, many women begin to both experience the rambunctious effects of hormones as more tolerable and grow more accustomed to simply being pregnant. This trimester is the easiest part of the pregnancy for most women, and it will hopefully come as a welcome respite for you. There are, however, no guarantees. But you may see a smile more often, and the fierce swings in mood may become less volatile. At the very least, things should not get worse.

Don't let that suggestion make you think changes in her are finished. She may begin to experience other pregnancy symptoms, like joint aches and unusual flexibility. Her body is going to start seriously adjusting to what it needs to be able to do at birth and bust that bowling ball through the eye of that needle. Relaxing plays a major role at this point which helps relax smooth muscle tissue and foster growth of the placenta. While flexibility may initially seem like a benefit, too much of a good thing can lead to loose joints, injuries, and problems performing seemingly simple tasks like walking or standing up. It is nothing to be tremendously alarmed about but something to be aware of. If mom has difficulty, she may need to take it easy to avoid a serious fall and may need your help — at times more than she would like to admit. Remain understanding and resist the urge to dote.

In all, the smorgasbord of symptoms, annoyances, and issues will probably pale in comparison and nearly seem to be a relief when compared to troubling nausea and relative insanity of the first trimester. It may well be that simple systematic desensitization to the initial onslaught has made her a better warrior, stoic to the mere, trifling challenges that emerged. She has made it this far and, as such, has fought an admirable and inescapable battle. Let her know that you admire her effort.

APPOINTMENT LOG

Date ....

Doctor's Name ....

Weight ....

Blood Pressure ....

To Do	Not To Do
....	....
....	....
....	....
....	....

Important Notes

....

....

....

....

....

MONTHLY JOURNAL

5 MINUTE JOURNALING

TOP 3 THINGS ABOUT THIS
MONTH

○

○

○

WHAT EMOTIONS HAVE YOU
FELT TODAY?

HOW WOULD YOU RATE THE
MONTH?

☆ ☆ ☆ ☆ ☆

WHAT INSPIRED YOU THE
MOST THIS MONTH?

3 THINGS I WISH FOR
TOMORROW

○

○

○

MONTHLY CHECK IN

TODAY I AM FEELING...

....

....

....

....

TODAY I AM GOING TO...

....

....

....

....

TODAY I AM LOOKING FORWARD TO...

....

....

....

....

MY AFFIRMATION TODAY

....

....

....

....

FINANCING AND BUDGETING

ITEM	Estimated	Actual	Purchased
Private pregnancy scans			
Decorating			
Crib/Cot			
Bed Linen			
Changing tables			
Baby monitor			
Play pen			
Rocking chair			
Stair gate			
Nursery furniture			
Baby bag			
Pram/Stroller			
Car seat			
Clothes			
Diapers			

FINANCING AND BUDGETING

ITEM	Estimated	Actual	Purchased
Bottles			
Sterilizer			

WEEK 15

Date .... **Baby Size** ....

Weight .... **Belly Measurement** ....

3 Things that happened this week

My childhood memory

Excited About

Challenges

Thoughts and Feelings

WEEK 16

Date ....   **Baby Size** ....

Weight ....   **Belly Measurement** ....

3 Things that happened this week   My childhood memory

Excited About   Challenges

Thoughts and Feelings

WEEK 17

Date .... **Baby Size** ....

Weight .... **Belly Measurement** ....

3 Things that happened this week

My childhood memory

Excited About

Challenges

Thoughts and Feelings

WEEK 18

Date ....   **Baby Size** ....

Weight ....   **Belly Measurement** ....

3 Things that happened this week   My childhood memory

Excited About   Challenges

Thoughts and Feelings

WEEK 19

Date ....   **Baby Size** ....

Weight ....   **Belly Measurement** ....

3 Things that happened this week   My childhood memory

Excited About   Challenges

Thoughts and Feelings

WEEK 20

Date ....   **Baby Size** ....

Weight ....   **Belly Measurement** ....

3 Things that happened this week

My childhood memory

Excited About

Challenges

Thoughts and Feelings

WEEK 21

Date _____   **Baby Size** _____

Weight _____   **Belly Measurement** _____

3 Things that happened this week   My childhood memory

Excited About   Challenges

Thoughts and Feelings

WEEK 22

Date .... **Baby Size** ....

Weight .... **Belly Measurement** ....

3 Things that happened this week

My childhood memory

Excited About

Challenges

Thoughts and Feelings

WEEK 23

Date ....   **Baby Size** ....

Weight ....   **Belly Measurement** ....

3 Things that happened this week

My childhood memory

Excited About

Challenges

Thoughts and Feelings

WEEK 24

Date .... **Baby Size** ....

Weight .... **Belly Measurement** ....

3 Things that happened this week   My childhood memory

Excited About   Challenges

Thoughts and Feelings

WEEK 25

Date .... **Baby Size** ....

Weight .... **Belly Measurement** ....

3 Things that happened this week

My childhood memory

Excited About

Challenges

Thoughts and Feelings

WEEK 26

Date ....

Baby Size ....

Weight ....

Belly Measurement ....

3 Things that happened this week

My childhood memory

Excited About

Challenges

Thoughts and Feelings

WEEK 27

Date ....

Baby Size ....

Weight ....

Belly Measurement ....

3 Things that happened this week

My childhood memory

Excited About

Challenges

Thoughts and Feelings

HOWS DAD DOING............

5 MINUTE JOURNALING

"My father used to say that it's never too late to do anything you wanted to do. And he said, 'You never know what you can accomplish until you try.'"

-Michael Jordan

THE 3ᴿᴰ TRIMESTER

WEEKS 28 TO 40

WHAT'S HAPPENING WITH BABY

Until this trimester, the baby has been doing more to grow in length than in girth. The baby will bulk up almost 50% over the trimester, and that comes in the way of organ development and shaping into what you recognize as a newborn. The eyes will open somewhere around week 28, and the fine hairs that have been protecting the skin for the past months will begin to shed. Right about week 35, the baby will shift its squished position so that its head will point down in order to exit head-first. It doesn't always happen, and that is considered a 'breach baby,' affecting about 5% of births. It can lead to complications, but it is really not a major concern in a situation with well-trained staff (doctors tend to be well-trained).

One of the most important things that will be going on throughout the trimester is the development of the lungs. One of the reasons premature babies have a rough time is that breathing is an issue because the lungs do not have the chance to form fully. Development goes on throughout the trimester; that is why it is best to go full-term. Even if mom is a little tired of being a free ride, she should not be doing anything to promote early labor unless at the suggestion of her physician.

The baby sleeps about 90% of the time and can REM sleep and dream. While sleeping most of the time, that does not mean there will be a lot of inactivity. Just like watching your dog chasing imaginary rabbits through the underbrush, the baby may exhibit activity even while sleeping. The baby will be practicing many things that will come in handy when finally escaping their holiday chamber. They may be smiling, frowning, and crying, and essentially taking baby steps in their development.

WHATS HAPPENING WITH YOUR PARTNER

Mom may experience premature contractions, known as Braxton Hicks contractions. It is probably best to just think of these as practice for the real thing. They can come on in various ways but will most likely be something like a cramp, a solid muscle contraction that mom is not doing intentionally. Of course, it is possible that labor can start prematurely, and it is best to be able to know the difference. Braxton Hicks contractions are irregular, and if there are clusters, they tend to get weaker. Often, they can be relaxed just by changing position (standing up, walking, etc.). Real contractions will not just be clusters that dissipate. They will keep coming in waves and will tend to get stronger. While that is still a bit vague, contractions for actual labor will come every 5 minutes, lasting one minute, for at least one hour. This may be accompanied by a discharge (e.g., water breaking). In other words, you need to take contractions seriously when they seem insistent, or like the last guest at a party that gets on the phone and calls some people to come over to liven things up a bit when the party sputters out.

The baby is active and kicking. There will be significant downtime, but there will be moments where the baby will seem to be trying to break out of the shell-like it is in an egg with limbs flying nearly like a kickboxer.

Mother's trips to the doctor will increase to about every two weeks and may be as frequent as once a week as the trimester comes to a close.

One thing she may be spending some particular amount of time within a variety of different ways is deliberate forms of nesting. This can be in the form of cleaning and preparing, fussing with the arrangement of baby things, watching cooking shows, reading about taking care of newborns, watching programming that seems peculiar to her normal regimen, etc. This more likely has to do with embracing the mindset of being a mom and having had nine months to appreciate that she is already responsible for the life of an entirely new human. Soon it will be kicking and screaming and laughing and being adorable in what seems more like real-time. Common sense says: "You've got to be ready; it's showtime."

APPOINTMENT LOG

Date ....

Doctor's Name ....

Weight ....

Blood Pressure ....

To Do

....

....

....

....

Not To Do

....

....

....

....

Important Notes

....

....

....

....

....

MONTHLY JOURNAL

5 MINUTE JOURNALING

TOP 3 THINGS ABOUT THIS MONTH

O ....

O ....

O ....

WHAT EMOTIONS HAVE YOU FELT TODAY?

HOW WOULD YOU RATE THE MONTH?

☆ ☆ ☆ ☆ ☆

WHAT INSPIRED YOU THE MOST THIS MONTH?

3 THINGS I WISH FOR TOMORROW

O ....

O ....

O ....

MONTHLY CHECK IN

TODAY I AM FEELING...

....

....

....

....

TODAY I AM GOING TO...

....

....

....

....

TODAY I AM LOOKING FORWARD TO...

....

....

....

....

MY AFFIRMATION TODAY

....

....

....

....

ITEMS TO PURCHASE

- ☐ Cot (plus mattress, sheets and blankets)
- ☐ Car seat
- ☐ Pram/buggy/travel system
- ☐ Six sleepsuits/ long sleeved suits
- ☐ Six vests/ short sleeved suits
- ☐ Two cardigans/ jackets
- ☐ Shawl or snow suit
- ☐ Hat, mittens and bootees
- ☐ Changing mat
- ☐ Nappies (get a full pack of Pampers nappies for free here)
- ☐ Nursing bra and breast pads
- ☐ Bottles/teats/bottle brush (only needed if not breastfeeding)
- ☐ Loads of bibs
- ☐ Plenty of towels/ flannels/ muslin squares (for bathing and dribbles!)
- ☐ Loads of kitchen roll and cotton wool pads
- ☐ Hairbrush
- ☐ Moses basket/ crib (plus mattress, sheets and blankets)
- ☐ Baby bath
- ☐ Baby box or bag
- ☐ Sling
- ☐ Bouncy chair
- ☐ Baby monitor
- ☐ Changing bag
- ☐ Breast pump
- ☐ Steam sterilizer
- ☐ Baby lotion
- ☐ Baby wipes
- ☐ Bath thermometer
- ☐ Nail scissors

WEEK 28

Date .... **Baby Size** ....

Weight .... **Belly Measurement** ....

3 Things that happened this week

My childhood memory

Excited About

Challenges

Thoughts and Feelings

WEEK 29

Date ....   **Baby Size** ....

Weight ....   **Belly Measurement** ....

3 Things that happened this week

My childhood memory

Excited About

Challenges

Thoughts and Feelings

WEEK 30

Date .... **Baby Size** ....

Weight .... **Belly Measurement** ....

3 Things that happened this week   My childhood memory

Excited About   Challenges

Thoughts and Feelings

WEEK 31

Date ....   **Baby Size** ....

Weight ....   **Belly Measurement** ....

3 Things that happened this week   My childhood memory

Excited About   Challenges

Thoughts and Feelings

WEEK 32

Date ....   **Baby Size** ....

Weight ....   **Belly Measurement** ....

3 Things that happened this week   My childhood memory

Excited About   Challenges

Thoughts and Feelings

WEEK 33

Date .... **Baby Size** ....

Weight .... **Belly Measurement** ....

3 Things that happened this week

My childhood memory

Excited About

Challenges

Thoughts and Feelings

WEEK 34

Date ....   **Baby Size** ....

Weight ....   **Belly Measurement** ....

3 Things that happened this week   My childhood memory

Excited About   Challenges

Thoughts and Feelings

WEEK 35

Date .... **Baby Size** ....

Weight .... **Belly Measurement** ....

3 Things that happened this week   My childhood memory

Excited About   Challenges

Thoughts and Feelings

WEEK 36

Date .... **Baby Size** ....

Weight .... **Belly Measurement** ....

3 Things that happened this week

My childhood memory

Excited About

Challenges

Thoughts and Feelings

WEEK 37

Date .... **Baby Size** ....

Weight .... **Belly Measurement** ....

3 Things that happened this week

My childhood memory

Excited About

Challenges

Thoughts and Feelings

WEEK 38

Date .... **Baby Size** ....

Weight .... **Belly Measurement** ....

3 Things that happened this week

My childhood memory

Excited About

Challenges

Thoughts and Feelings

WEEK 39

Date .... **Baby Size** ....

Weight .... **Belly Measurement** ....

3 Things that happened this week

My childhood memory

Excited About

Challenges

Thoughts and Feelings

WEEK 40

Date .... **Baby Size** ....

Weight .... **Belly Measurement** ....

3 Things that happened this week

My childhood memory

Excited About

Challenges

Thoughts and Feelings

HOWS DAD DOING.............

5 MINUTE JOURNALING

"The best way of training the young
is to train yourself at the same time.
Not to admonish them,
but to be seen never doing that of
which you would admonish them."

-Plato

THE 4ᵀᴴ TRIMESTER

WHAT IS HAPPENING WITH BABY

Baby just got plopped out of its comfortable, warm nest into the bright lights and big city of a hospital room. It is a lot to get used to when compared to the muffled, dull plodding of the womb. No wonder most of them start crying almost immediately. The baby is tended to with any special care concerns, but mostly the focus will be on acclimating the child to mom and the new real world. The baby will be weighed and measured, given antibiotic eye drops, and a shot of vitamin K. The latter helps normalize blood clotting. They will take the baby's footprints for records and additional ID. Before even leaving the birthing room, mom, dad, and baby will all get ID bracelets that they need to have at all times to be sure the parents are reunited with the correct children. The goal is to make the nightmare of a potential mix-up something that is nearly impossible. There were tragic records in the past of babies being swapped at birth, but gladly the practice has evolved. In extreme cases, DNA could be used to identify the proper parents of a child.

Post-birth tests include hearing tests, blood tests, and observation for congenital heart defects. If required, the baby may be tested for HIV and hepatitis. If it is a boy and the option for circumcision is selected, it may be performed within the first two days. A practice becoming more common is having parents return after a week or two for the procedure.

Once you are out of the hospital, the baby no longer has the automated support system and protection of the mother's body. The hospital staff will not trail you home, and the baby is totally dependent on its parents for survival. Intending to that level of care, neither parent is likely to get a lot of sleep, and that will remain the case for some time until things settle into a routine.

WHATS HAPPENING WITH MY PARTNER

Your partner just went through a sudden colossal change in her physique. She might be the type just to shrug it off, or she may find the shift somewhat disorienting. She may be superhuman if she isn't at least a little light-headed, extremely relieved, or even giddy immediately after the birth.

Mom and baby will remain in recovery for two to four days, depending on whether it was natural childbirth or not. This may vary due to hospital policies. Regardless, mom's body will have to begin a process of repair. She needs to eat healthily, stay hydrated, and care for her state until her strength returns.

Rely on her to choose whether or not to accept visitors. People may have stayed in the waiting room hoping to hear the good news, but that does not mean they should automatically be admitted after birth to be the first to see the baby. Your partner will likely be exhausted, not feeling that she looks her best (despite and because of the sudden loss of 15 pounds) or may just need some downtime to get it in her head that the process is complete. She will probably be happy to have fewer doctors poking and prodding as if she were a science experiment and learning how to be a new mom is the premiere item on her list.

Breastfeeding is new to her, and the first attempts may be as soon as an hour after birth. There can be issues here as likely as not with the baby learning mom's anatomy and mom having zero experience. Hospitals will likely have a specialist on staff to consult for breastfeeding issues. It is important for mother and child to have that time to bond.

There are likely to be mood swings brought on by exhaustion, hormones, and simple emotional reactions to reality. Joy, disbelief, even missing having her baby inside her can come on her in a moment. The fluctuations may wear off in just a few weeks or may linger. In extreme cases, it may evolve into post-partum depression. Suspicion of the latter should be evaluated. In all, the hope is that things gradually return to normal for her and you over the next six weeks or so. Be her careful watchman, and don't assume it is time to leave your post.

APPOINTMENT LOG

Date ....

Doctor's Name ....

Weight ....

Blood Pressure ....

To Do	Not To Do
....	....
....	....
....	....
....	....

Important Notes

....

....

....

....

....

MONTHLY JOURNAL

5 MINUTE JOURNALING

TOP 3 THINGS ABOUT THIS MONTH

○ _____

○ _____

○ _____

WHAT INSPIRED YOU THE MOST THIS MONTH?

WHAT EMOTIONS HAVE YOU FELT TODAY?

HOW WOULD YOU RATE THE MONTH?

☆ ☆ ☆ ☆ ☆

3 THINGS I WISH FOR TOMORROW

○ _____

○ _____

○ _____

MONTHLY CHECK IN

TODAY I AM FEELING...

....

....

....

....

TODAY I AM GOING TO...

....

....

....

....

TODAY I AM LOOKING FORWARD TO...

....

....

....

....

MY AFFIRMATION TODAY

....

....

....

....

HOSPITAL CHECKLIST

Baby Bag

- [ ] Bodysuits or vests
- [ ] Sleepsuits
- [ ] Hats
- [ ] Scratch mittens
- [ ] Socks or booties
- [ ] Nappies
- [ ] Cotton wool balls or pads
- [ ] Blankets
- [ ] Muslin squares
- [ ] Bottles if not provided
- [ ] A snowsuit if it's cold.
- [ ] Car seat

Mother-to-be checklist

- [ ] Maternity notes.
- [ ] Birth plan, if you've made one.
- [ ] A comfy, loose outfit for labor that you can move around in and that won't make you too hot.
- [ ] Chill-out kit including books, magazines, music
- [ ] A fan or water spray to cool you down.
- [ ] A phone and charger
- [ ] Healthy snacks and drinks.
- [ ] Your own pillow, possibly a giant pregnancy one.
- [ ] A TENS machine and batteries if you want to use one and if your hospital doesn't provide one.
- [ ] Any medication you're taking.
- [ ] Your wash bag with your toothbrush, toothpaste, hairbrush, soap, hair ties, and other toiletries.
- [ ] Aromatherapy oils, especially if you have been using them during pregnancy, e.g. for hypnobirthing.

What essentials shall I pack in my hospital bag for after the birth?

Once labour's done and dusted and you're chilling out with your new arrival, you'll need a whole host of other things.

Bring these in your bag:

- [ ] Large sanitary or maternity pads
- [ ] Large comfy knickers (or disposable ones)
- [ ] Towels
- [ ] Dressing gown
- [ ] Slippers or flip-flops
- [ ] Comfy, maternity-sized outfit to wear home
- [ ] Cash – you might need it for parking or to grab a magazine or emergency chocolate bar
- [ ] iPad or tablet.
- [ ] And if you're planning to breastfeed, add:
- [ ] Nursing bras
- [ ] Breast pads
- [ ] Front-opening nighties or pajama tops.

Dads to be a checklist

- [ ] Snacks
- [ ] Cash
- [ ] A change of clothes
- [ ] A wash bag
- [ ] A camping mattress if there is room for them to stay over
- [ ] A book or something to distract the mum to be if you're relaxing in the early stages.

BABY MONTH ONE

Date .... **Baby Size/weight** ....

3 Things that happened this
month

My childhood memory

Excited About

Challenges

Thoughts and Feelings

BABY MONTH TWO

Date .... **Baby Size/weight** ....

3 Things that happened this
month

My childhood memory

Excited About

Challenges

Thoughts and Feelings

BABY MONTH THREE

Date .... **Baby Size/weight** ....

3 Things that happened this
month

My childhood memory

Excited About

Challenges

Thoughts and Feelings

HOWS DAD DOING.............

5 MINUTE JOURNALING

"Father is the noblest title a man can be given.

It is more than a biological role.

It signifies a patriarch, a leader, an exemplar, a confidant, a teacher, a hero, a friend."

-Robert L. Backman

Baby Weight	....
Baby Height	....
Date of Birth	....
Time of Birth	....
My First Words	....
My Favorite Toy	....
My Favorite Food	....

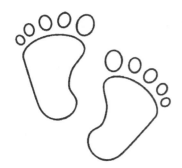

I would be glad to hear your feedback about this Journal, both from the perspective of how it applied to your experience and what you learned from your real-life experience that could have been included here. Feel free to email me at: http://williamhardingauthor.com/.

If you think the Journal was helpful and that it is worthy of a nice review, please leave one on Amazon or your venue of choice. This will help dads that you don't even know to prepare for this phase of their life and look forward to enjoying their future.

Thanks for reading this work. I look forward to creating more in the future.

You may not be ready to do it again just yet, and your partner may not be either, but like everything that slides into the rear-view mirror of life, you can always look back with a greater appreciation.

Made in the USA
Coppell, TX
03 April 2023

15124170R00164